PENGUIN BOOKS
WISE AND OTHERWISE

Sudha Murty was born in 1950 in Shiggaon in north Karnataka. She did her MTech in computer science, and is now the chairperson of the Infosys Foundation. A prolific writer in English and Kannada, she has written novels, technical books, travelogues, collections of short stories and non-fiction pieces, and four books for children. Her books have been translated into all the major Indian languages.

Sudha Murty was the recipient of the R.K. Narayan Award for Literature and the Padma Shri in 2006, and the Attimabbe Award from the government of Karnataka for excellence in Kannada literature in 2011.

Also by the same author

SUDHA MURTY

WISE AND OTHERWISE

A Salute to Life

PENGUIN BOOKS

PENGUIN BOOKS

USA | Canada | UK | Ireland | Australia
New Zealand | India | South Africa | China

Penguin Books is part of the Penguin Random House group of companies
whose addresses can be found at global.penguinrandomhouse.com

Published by Penguin Random House India Pvt. Ltd
7th Floor, Infinity Tower C, DLF Cyber City,
Gurgaon 122 002, Haryana, India

First published by East West Books (Madras) Pvt. Ltd 2002
Revised edition first published by Penguin Books India 2006

Copyright © Sudha Murty 2002, 2006

44 43 42 41 40 39 38 37

ISBN 9780143062226

For sale in the Indian Subcontinent only

Typeset in Sabon by Mantra Virtual Services, New Delhi
Printed at Replika Press Pvt. Ltd, India

www.penguin.co.in

For the 'shirtless people of India'
who have taught me so much
about my country

Contents

ACKNOWLEDGEMENTS

I want to thank Mr T.J.S. George, for having kindly consented to write the Foreword. I also thank Penguin India for their long-standing support, especially V.K. Karthika, who showed keen interest in publishing a revised and updated edition of this book.

But readers, ultimately I thank you. You are the best judge and my source of inspiration. Without your support, I cease to be a writer.

Bangalore   Sudha Murty
March 2006

We are heirs to the tradition of seeing human quality as *sattwa*, *rajas* or *tamas*. This is a beautifully Indian way of expressing a metaphysical concept familiar to other civilizations as well: of all God's creations, man alone has a choice between good and evil, and he reaps his rewards according to what he chooses.

Few set out consciously to perform *sattwik* work. Fewer still deliberately desire a life of *tamas*. Some could even start out with *tamas* or *rajas* and elevate themselves to *sattwa*. All this would be attributed to the larger cosmic scheme of karma. Jamshedji Tata appears to have had only a *sattwik* view of life and work—laying an industrial foundation for his country, starting educational and research institutions, and setting up a network of charities when such ideas were unknown. On the other hand, Alfred Nobel spent his genius inventing dynamite and smokeless gunpowder, which would all become agents of mass destruction. Then, perhaps stung by the implications of his life's achievements, he put the fortune he made to *sattwik* use by instituting the Nobel Prizes, as recognition for noble work.

Sudha Murty was not meant to hide her light under a

housewife's bushel. She was born with teacher's blood in her veins, and teaching, she learned early, was a vocation that could help shape the world. But she did not remain just another face in the teaching crowd either. Unseen but clearly felt forces propelled her into unfamiliar territory. For one thing, she married a man with socialist blood in his veins. For another, when the benedictions of capitalism came their way, the instincts of the teacher and the socialist combined to take them into an orbit of public service for public good. While remaining a teacher, wife, mother and very much the woman next door, Sudha Murty turned into an institution.

She has built no edifices. No public announcements accompany her work. No statues or tablets or archways proclaim her presence. She goes into tribal forests, into hamlets ravaged by poverty, into communities devastated by disease. She discovers the deserving on her own. The assistance she supplies meets the demand she sees. Frustrations, obstacles and red tape do not slow her down. Even human greed, a great deal of which she faces in the course of her work, does not dissuade her. Her work is her mission. She does her duty in the style and the spirit of the *karma yogi*.

This book gives a clear account of both her work and her approach to it. An accomplished storyteller in Kannada, Sudha wrote for the first time in English to inaugurate a fortnightly column in the *New Sunday Express*. She focused on her personal experiences, her travels and her encounters with ordinary people with extraordinary minds. The column attracted instant attention because of its freshness and its directness. Evidently, she was writing not with her pen but with her heart. It was clear from the start that these anecdotal insights into human nature merited a format more enduring than journalism could provide.

It would be a pity, though, if the benefits of these stories stop with the pleasure of reading them. Sudha Murty is nothing if not a message. By turning the success of Infosys into an opportunity to serve the less privileged, she has conveyed an idea to others similarly positioned. Corporate championship of social amelioration programmes on the one hand and intellectual creativity on the other is common in advanced countries, but rare in ours. There is nothing in India comparable to the foundations associated with families of great wealth in the West, such as Ford, Rockefeller and Nuffield. The most respected of them, the MacArthur Foundation, gives out what have come to be known as 'genius awards'. No one knows about this because no publicity of any kind is given to it. Yet it quietly identifies people of great talent—like A.K. Ramanujan—and quietly gives them funds to proceed with their chosen work. Thus is excellence, the true worth of a nation, nurtured by society. Sudha Murty's work will be complete only when the tradition of grand foundations rises in India to help the needy, recognize originality, facilitate intellectual inquiry and generally inspire the pursuit of greatness.

T.J.S. George
Editorial Adviser
The New Indian Express

HONESTY COMES FROM THE HEART

One bright June morning three years ago, I was reading my Kannada newspaper as usual. It was the day the Secondary School Leaving Certificate results had been published. While columns of roll numbers filled the inside pages, the list of rank holders and their photographs took up almost the entire front page.

I have a great fascination for rank holders. Rank is not merely an index of one's intelligence, it also indicates the hard work and perseverance that students have put in to reach their goal. My background—I was brought up in a professor's family—and my own experience as a teacher have led me to believe this.

Of all the photographs in that morning's newspaper, one boy's snapshot caught my attention. I could not take my eyes off him. He was frail and pale, but there was an endearing sparkle in his eyes. I wanted to know more about him. I read that his name was Hanumanthappa and that he had secured the eighth rank. That was all the information I could gather.

The next day, to my surprise, his photograph was published again, this time with an interview. With growing interest I learned that Hanumanthappa was a coolie's son, the oldest of five children. They belonged to a tribal group.

He was unable to study further, he said in the interview, because he lived in a village and his father, the sole breadwinner, earned only Rs 40 a day.

I felt sorry for this bright boy. Most of us send our children to tuitions and to coaching classes, we buy them reference books and guides, and provide the best possible facilities for them without considering the cost. But it was different for Hanumanthappa of Rampura. He had excelled in spite of being denied some of the basic necessities of life.

While I was thinking about him with the newspaper still in my hands, I gazed at a mango tree in my neighbour's compound. It looked its best with fresh bark, tender green leaves glistening with dewdrops and mangoes that were about to ripen in a few days. Beyond the tree was a small potted plant that, I noticed, had remained almost the same ever since it had been potted. It was a calm morning. The air was cool and fresh. My thoughts were running free. The continuous whistle of our pressure cooker broke the silence, reminding me that half an hour had passed.

Hanumanthappa's postal address was provided in the interview. Without wasting much time, I took a postcard and wrote to him. I wrote only two lines, saying that I was interested in meeting him and asking whether he could come to Bangalore. Just then my father, ever a practical man, returned from his morning walk. He read the postcard and said, 'Where will he have the money to come so far? If you want him to come here, send some money for his bus fare plus a little extra to buy himself a decent set of clothes.'

So I added a third line to say that I would pay for his travel and some clothes. Within four days I received a similar postcard in reply. Two sentences: in the first he thanked me for the letter, in the second he expressed his willingness to come to Bangalore and meet me. Immediately, I sent him some money and details of my office address.

When he finally arrived in our office, he looked like a frightened calf that had lost its way. It must have been his first trip to Bangalore. He was humble. He wore a clean shirt and trousers, and his hair was neatly parted and combed. The sparkle in his eyes was still there.

I got straight to the point. 'We are happy about your academic performance. Do you want to study further? We would like to sponsor you. This means we will pay your fees for any course of study you wish to take up— wherever it may be.'

He did not answer.

My senior colleague, who was in the office with me, interrupted with a smile, 'Don't go at the speed of bits and bytes. Let the boy understand what you are suggesting. He can give us his answer at the end of the day.'

When Hanumanthappa was ready to return home, he said in a low and steady tone, 'Madam, I want to pursue my studies at the Teachers' Training College in Bellary. That is the one nearest to my village.'

I agreed instantly but spoke to him a little more to find out whether there was any other course he preferred. I was trying to make it clear to him that we would pay the fees for any course he might choose. The boy, however, seemed to know exactly what he wanted.

'How much money should I send you per month? Does the college have a hostel facility?' I asked.

He said he would get back to me after collecting the correct details. Two days later, he wrote to us in his beautiful handwriting that he would require approximately Rs 300 per month. He planned to take a room on rent and share it with a friend. The two boys would cook for themselves in order to keep their expenses down.

I sent him Rs 1,800 to cover his expenses for six months. He acknowledged my draft without delay and expressed his gratitude.

Time passed. One day, I suddenly remembered that I had to pay Hanumanthappa for the next six months, so I sent him another draft for Rs 1,800.

This too was duly acknowledged, but I was surprised to find some currency notes in the envelope along with his letter. 'Madam,' he had written, 'it is kind of you to have sent me money for the next six months. But I was not in Bellary for the last two months. One month, our college was closed for holidays and during the next month, there was a strike. So I stayed at home for those two months. My expenditure during these months was less than Rs 300 per month. Therefore, I am sending you the Rs 300 that I have not used for the last two months. Kindly accept this amount.'

I was taken aback. Such poverty and yet such honesty. Hanumanthappa knew I expected no account of the money sent to him for his monthly expenses, yet he had made it a point to return the balance money. Unbelievable but true!

Experience has taught me that honesty is not the mark of any particular class nor is it related to education or wealth. It cannot be taught at any university. In most people, it springs naturally from the heart.

I did not know how to react to this simple village boy's honesty. I just prayed that God would continue to bestow the best on Hanumanthappa and his family.

2

On Human Foibles

Many years ago, I was working as a Chief System Analyst. The job involved a lot of travelling for project work, sometimes to a small village, sometimes to a neighbouring city. Often, work compelled me to travel on holidays as well.

One particular Friday, I was looking forward to the weekend. The coming Monday was a holiday for some festival and taking advantage of the long weekend, my sisters and I had decided to meet at our grandmother's house in our native Shiggaon. Sunday was a full-moon night and a special moonlight dinner was going to be arranged for us. Moonlight dinners are favourite family occasions for the people of northern Karnataka.

We were all in a hurry to wind up for the day when I heard someone calling out, 'Kulkarni! Can you come to my office?'

My heart sank. It was my boss calling me by my maiden name, and judging by his tone, the matter was urgent. Even though I was on my way out of the office, I stopped to enquire what he wanted.

'Sorry for disturbing you, but your service is required urgently,' he said, handing over a letter for me to read. It said that I had to visit a project site within the next two days.

'No problem at all, sir. I shall attend to it,' I said. I was used to working throughout the week, so cancelling my travel plans didn't bother me. My work gave me more happiness than any celebration or outing.

The next morning, I left for the small town where the project was based. By the time I reached the town it was already noon, but it looked as though the day had just begun there. The shops were just opening and folks were setting out to work.

As I was walking from the bus stand, a young lad hurried towards me and said, 'Sorry I am late, ma'am. I was supposed to receive you at the bus stop.' He was our clients' representative and had come to take me to their office.

We reached the office after a few minutes' walk. It was a small office. Though by no means modern, it was neatly furnished with some old but reconditioned furniture, everything in its right place. They were all waiting for me and I felt comfortable as I sat down. The cool buttermilk they offered me was most refreshing.

Before beginning my work, I was introduced to a neatly dressed young man who was supposed to coordinate with me. He was quite well-mannered and seemed very confident and bright. I was pleasantly surprised to see the good quality of his work. It had a professional touch. I was told that he was the most well-read man in that town.

He had documented his work very well and efficiently. Because of this, our job was completed sooner than expected. I did not forget to compliment him when I was about to leave. He went pink at my appreciation and insisted that I join him for tea at his residence nearby.

His house was also well kept. By teatime his conversation had taken on a personal note. He talked about his parents, his job. He introduced his wife and two-year-old son. He spoke with admiration about his wife's cooking, her beautiful voice, her achievements during her school days. Then he called for his son who immediately came in and stood by my side with folded arms, almost as if he had been trained to do so. As soon as his father asked him to recite a rhyme, he started to do so in his clear, childish voice.

I acknowledged his recitation by nodding my head. The father did not seem satisfied with such nominal recognition of his son's talents. He asked the child to identify all the letters of the alphabet from an old chart hanging on the wall. These are things that children usually hate to do, yet parents continue to force them. Poor kids!

The demonstration in my host's house went on for nearly half an hour until the child began to show signs of restlessness and irritability. The mother, wisely, took him away to the kitchen, hopefully to reward him with a chocolate or a biscuit.

I realized that the father was expecting to hear some compliment from me about his son. 'Your child is very bright for his age,' I said.

'Naturally! I have trained him like that from infancy,' he said with pride. It sounded like he had been training his two-year-old child from the day of his birth!

'So you feel that it is only by training that a child can

become bright like this?' I asked.

'No, no. Heredity and genes also play an important role. My son has taken after me.' His face shone with pride and I was curious to hear more. After all, I had an hour to spare before my bus departed.

'You must have been a good student in your college days?' I probed.

'Yes, I was always a first-ranker in my school and college days,' he replied, clearly appreciative of himself.

'Where did you graduate from?'

'I graduated from BVB Engineering College, Hubli.'

I became alert. I knew Hubli. It was my college. 'Which year?' I asked.

'In 1972, with the first rank.'

'Did you secure the gold medal also?' I persisted.

'Yes, I did obtain the gold medal for that year,' he said, glowing with self satisfaction.

By this time I was able to size him up quite clearly. And what I saw saddened me.

'May I see your gold medal?' I inquired.

Suddenly, the mood in the room changed. 'Why? Don't you believe me?' His voice was uncertain.

'No, I just want to see the gold medal you secured in 1972,' I repeated.

'It is very precious to me and so I have kept it in a bank locker,' he said.

I did not give up. 'Which bank?'

'Why should I give you such details?' he demanded, annoyed with my persistence.

Everything was clear by now. I think it was clear to

him too. The warmth of hospitality was gone. It was time for me to go.

While walking towards the door, I said, 'I don't have to know any of the details about your bank or gold medal. It's none of my business. But I am sure that the medal cannot be with you.'

'How can you say that? And that too so confidently?' He was quite angry by now.

'Because,' I told him sadly, 'I secured that gold medal in 1972 and only one gold medal is awarded each year.'

He was stunned by this revelation and stared blankly at me. I looked at him and asked gently, 'You are bright. You are good in your job. Why do you have to lie? What do you gain from it?'

The click of the front door shutting behind me was the only reply I received.

3

IN SAHYADRI HILLS, A LESSON IN HUMILITY

I love travelling. Be it a tiny village, a drought-hit area, a deserted mountain top, a dense forest or even a monument in Egypt or China—I enjoy going to different places.

On one occasion, I went to the Sahyadri Hills, a densely forested region in Karnataka. It had been drizzling the whole day. Though forests are difficult to negotiate during the rains, especially due to the presence of those dreaded leeches, one ought to visit them during the rainy season to get the most out of them. The mild smell of exotic trees, shrubs and flowers; the chirping of different kinds of birds; the gentle whistle of the unpolluted breeze—these are joys that can never be experienced in any town or city.

I was there to visit a tribal village school deep in the forest area. The charitable trust with which I am connected wanted to help improve the school. Thandas (as local groups of tribals are called) are delightful. Normally there is a headman in each Thanda known as the Thandappa. He is the senior-most man of the tribe and is considered the supreme power, almost a living God. All are beholden to him. He practises the customs taught to him in his childhood and everyone follows them.

There was a downpour when I reached the village.

The rain, the glistening leaves and the strong smell of wild flowers made me feel as though I was on a different planet. But I never felt like an intruder. Not even when I reached the school after a long walk and every villager stood by staring at me.

Reaching the school was an adventure in itself. I saw a lady walking with rhythmic grace despite the three pots of water balanced on her head. I stopped her and asked, 'Which way should I go to reach the school?' She made an exclamatory sound, stared at me and walked away. Perhaps she didn't want to talk to a stranger, especially one from a town. Or perhaps she didn't understand my language.

I then approached an old man who was weaving a cane basket while humming a folk song. I knelt in front of him and asked in a loud and clear tone, 'Where is the school?' Curiosity was written all over his face and he seemed anxious to ask me all kinds of questions. But he didn't. He simply said something in his dialect and indicated directions with his hand.

The school was an old thatched building, probably built by the tribals themselves. It was a primary school. I could see a few children playing outside, while others were busy under a shed-like shelter doing something with leaves and straws.

I walked in and found a small room with two chairs, two tables, and a blackboard with a pot of water beside it. There were no electric lights or fans. Instead, a small shutterless opening served as the window. This was the only source of ventilation in the room.

It appeared to be the office room but there was no one there. I did not find any staff around. While I was looking for someone, an elderly man walked up to me and asked what I wanted. I introduced myself and told him that I had come to see what help we could provide the school. His response, however, didn't seem very encouraging. I thought I might be able to communicate better if I first put him at ease, so I started asking him about his life.

It turned out that he was the live-in watchman-cum-peon of the school. He would double as a tour guide sometimes. But he was not a paid employee of either the school or the government. His grandson was studying in the school free of cost in return for the services which the old man rendered. How long had he been living there? 'For many years,' he replied simply. He lived in a small hut in the courtyard of the school.

By now his attitude towards me was slightly more encouraging, so I gently turned the conversation to the affairs of the school. He said that the state government ran the school; there were two teachers and around fifty students who came from far and near. There was no compulsory uniform. I was impressed by the number of children who attended the school. After all, their parents were unschooled themselves and the living conditions were harsh. Yet there was a willingness to educate their children.

'What are the difficulties you face in running this school?'

The old man didn't say much by way of reply. He just took me to a cottage nearby and introduced me to the

Thandappa, who seemed to be more than ninety years old. He was happy to see me.

I asked him the same question: 'What problems do you face in running the school?'

Commuting to school was difficult during the rains, he said. Besides, the school clothes wouldn't dry in the rainy season—the simplest of problems and a familiar one, too. During the course of my work, I have listened to many such problems from many such people.

After acquiring a fair understanding of the people and their lives, I departed, not forgetting to thank them for their cooperation. I decided to return with some umbrellas and clothes for the children.

When I went again, it was winter. The rains were over. Now the scene was transformed. It was paradise. There was no mud and no frogs croaking. Birds were cooing. The sky was clear. Many rare flowers had bloomed. I met the same Thandappa. He recognized me and greeted me with a smile. His eyes seemed to welcome me warmly.

'Please accept these things which I have brought for the children here. Last time, I didn't know what to give them,' I said, handing over a big bag to him.

The Thandappa hesitated. I wondered whether he was feeling embarrassed. I told him, 'You have not asked for any gift from me. I brought this myself. It will help the children during the rains. Please get the clothes stitched according to their size.'

He walked into his hut without saying a word.

'What do you want to learn?' I asked some children who were standing nearby.

No one answered. After a lot of persuasion, a few youngsters came closer, but they were still too shy to talk. I went on coaxing them and ultimately one of them said, 'We've heard about computers but we have not seen them, except on TV. We want to learn about computers. Do you have any book about computers that is written in Kannada?'

Having been brought up in a teacher's family and being a teacher myself, I was delighted to hear what these children had to say. Their ideas were surprisingly fresh and modern despite the fact that they belonged to such a backward region.

I told them that I would look for such books in Bangalore. If I didn't find any, I promised that I would write a book for them myself. They seemed pleased and I was extremely happy. By that time the Thandappa had returned from inside his hut. He held a bottle of red liquid in his hands.

'Amma,' he said, presenting the bottle to me, 'we do not know what you like and what you drink at home. This is a very special drink that we prepare during summer in this forest area. We extract juice from a wild red fruit and store it. It lasts for at least two rainy seasons. Nothing is added to the juice. It is good for health. Add some of this juice to a cup of water and stir it before drinking.'

I was embarrassed. How could I accept a gift from these poor people? They themselves did not seem to have enough to eat and drink. Moreover, I had gone on a mission to give, not to take. I thought it over and politely declined the gift.

The Thandappa then said gravely, 'Amma, then we cannot accept your gift either. Our ancestors have lived in this forest for generations and they have taught us their ways. When you want to give us something, we accept; but only when we can give something to you too. Unless you take our gift, we cannot take the things you have brought for us.'

I was shocked, embarrassed, and humbled. Nothing in my experience had prepared me for this. The usual pattern is for people to express gratitude when a charitable organization provides some assistance. I have come across complaints too. When a group or organization has many problems and we help solve one of them, it is not unusual for the recipients of our help to grumble about what has been left undone rather than show gratitude for what has been accomplished. There have even been cases where recipients have complained about the amount of help given to them. I have taken all this in my stride, finding fulfilment in the giving, not in the responses.

Here in the Sahyadri forest was an old man, a tribal with no schooling, practising a highly principled philosophy of life—give when you take; do not take without giving. This was culture at its best. I smiled and gracefully accepted his gift.

The Thandappa rose even further in my esteem when he remarked with a twinkle, 'There is a grace in accepting also.'

4

DEATH WITHOUT GRIEF

Life has become so busy in a big city like Bangalore that we hardly get to know our neighbours. We are all so busy with our work that often we do not even have the time to think.

Once, I came to know that someone in my neighbours' family had died. I didn't know these neighbours well, but my mother wanted me to visit them to offer our condolences. It is the custom in our society after all, she insisted.

I agreed, but did not find the time to pay a call for several days. Days usually dawned to a rush of busy schedules and night-time was not considered appropriate for such visits. So my condolence visit just got postponed again and again. However, I didn't give up the idea and continued to think that I would find some time to call on our bereaved neighbours.

Ten days passed. I felt so guilty that one Sunday I decided that I would visit my neighbour at any cost. I only knew the man of the family, albeit very casually.

As I walked through their gate, I could hear the loud beat of a popular Kannada film song. There were children playing hide-and-seek in the spacious garden. Some men and women, who seemed to have come from the village, were sitting in the garden and chatting in a carefree way.

For a moment, I thought that I had come to the wrong house. Such mistakes do happen once in a while. Some time ago, for example, I had gone to attend the wedding of my student at the Sagar group of wedding halls near the Ashoka Pillar in Jayanagar. There are four wedding halls in a row. I had forgotten in which hall my student's wedding was to take place. However, I knew that the bride's name was Usha. When I looked at the flower-bedecked welcome arches, which mentioned the names of the couple, I was taken aback. In two of the arches, the bride's name was given as Usha. I could not remember the groom's name. I did not know what to do and just stood between the two halls waiting to see a familiar face.

Here in my neighbour's house, the music and gay atmosphere was so unexpected that I thought of going back home to ascertain the correct address from my mother. Just then, the head of the family came out and saw me. He looked excited as he called out, 'What a surprise! Please come inside. I think you are coming to our house for the first time.'

I had no choice but to go inside. As he went in and called his wife, I observed the big house and the way they had furnished it. The living room was quite large. There was a TV with a VCR in one corner. *Kaho Na Pyar Hai*, a popular Hindi film, was playing on the video. The room was packed with so many youngsters that they managed to occupy a big mat, three sofas and even the entire carpet. All of them were watching the movie with great interest. There was no place for us to sit, but the man of the house managed to move a few kids to the floor and made some room for me to sit down.

The handsome actor Hrithik Roshan was dancing on the television screen. The youngsters around me were all tapping their feet.

A servant arrived bearing a tray of snacks and a cup of tea. I was now faced with a problem. Considering the nature of my visit, I wondered whether it would be appropriate for me to partake of the snacks. My instinct told me that it would not be correct for me to eat, but I also realized that it might seem rude of me to refuse. So I found an acceptable excuse. 'I have not yet had my bath. I cannot eat now,' I said.

That of course did not solve my real problem. The atmosphere in the house had a festive air. There was no trace of grief or mourning at all. How then could I start with my condolences? It looked like my neighbours were having a family get-together for an engagement ceremony or a birthday party. And here I was, bearing a message of condolence.

Just then the lady of the house came in. Both husband and wife sat on a sofa adjacent to my chair. They started the conversation. 'We are very happy about your work. Every day we talk about you. We are proud of it.'

I was puzzled. Why on earth should they talk about me every day? I don't talk about anybody every day. Not even about my husband. What work were they talking about? Was it my writing or my social work?

They noticed my silence but continued talking animatedly. 'How is your husband? He is really a great man.'

I was surprised that my husband should feature in the conversation, considering that this family was supposed to be in mourning.

Both husband and wife were eager to talk. The wife said, 'The other day I saw you. You were wearing a beautiful sari. I thought it was a Patola sari. Was it a Patola or an Orissa sari? Both have similar patterns.'

I really did not remember which sari she was talking about. 'Maybe Orissa,' I said noncommitally.

She beamed and said triumphantly, 'See, I am right. I told Suman the same thing. She does a lot of work in Orissa so she must have purchased that sari from there. What a beautiful colour combination!'

Now, it was the turn of the husband. 'Your company is doing very well. One of the few companies that is independent of the dotcom wave. I suggested to a few of my friends that they should study the trend of IT companies in the last six months.'

This was not related to me. Maybe my husband could comment on the trend, but he was not present.

Now the wife took over. 'What is the admission procedure at your college? Is it possible to get admission with only an 85 per cent score in the tenth standard?'

'Not in SSLC but in ICSE,' the husband clarified hastily, referring to different boards of school education.

'I do not know, I am not on the admission committee,' I replied.

And so it went on. There seemed to be no end to the conversation.

After some time, I found myself wondering who had

died. As far as I remembered, it was the man's mother who had passed away. The old lady had been a friend of my mother's. But I did not know how to raise the topic. Suppose it had been the wife's mother who had died? I had to be careful.

I am sure they noticed my silence, but they were intent on pulling me into the conversation. I was feeling very uncomfortable about the whole thing. By this time I had realized that it was unlikely that I was going to get an opportunity to offer my condolences. But before I left, I wanted to make a last, sincere effort to fulfil the purpose of my visit.

It was only when we neared the gate that I hesitantly raised the topic.

'I heard your mother was not well . . .'

Before the husband could answer, his wife replied, 'Yes. My mother-in-law was not well for a very long time. But we had a lot of problems. She was too old-fashioned and would not adjust. These men go off to work and never understand the difficulties of women at home.'

She continued to complain bitterly about her mother-in-law while the husband looked on guiltily.

'She suffered a lot,' he intervened at one point.

'Actually, we suffered a lot,' the wife interrupted indignantly. 'Of late she was bedridden with a stroke. To look after such people in a place like Bangalore, one requires servants and you know how difficult and expensive it is to get a good servant. I was so tired of looking after her. It was good riddance.' The lady's tone was harsh and cold.

'Death solved the problem for all of us. My mother was finally relieved from all her suffering,' the husband concluded.

I came away saddened and disturbed by my visit.

Have our lives become so busy that grief has become proportionate to the usefulness of the loved one we have lost?

5

WHEN THE MOP COUNT DID NOT TALLY

My father was a doctor and a very popular professor of obstetrics and gynaecology. He would never bore his class with long lectures. Every now and then he would tell his students stories, usually real-life incidents, in order to liven up his lectures. As a result, his classes were well attended and lively.

I once asked him, 'Why do you tell so many stories in a medical class?'

'Don't you know why the Panchatantra was written?' he asked in reply.

'But the Panchatantra is not relevant,' I insisted. 'It's for young schoolgoing children, not for medical students.'

My father didn't agree. 'If I use stories, then it's easy for my students to understand. Moreover, one cannot hold a student's attention for more than forty-five minutes at a stretch even if the lecture is interesting. So, if I add stories, I can stretch their concentration span for up to two hours.'

The following was one of his stories. My father says that the incident actually took place in England.

The operation theatre is popularly called 'OT' among medical professionals. An OT nurse is considered a very responsible and powerful person in a hospital. She is highly respected by doctors and surgeons. Normally, only senior and experienced nurses are given the post of an OT nurse.

Once, a very popular and senior surgeon was operating on a patient. It happened that the regular OT nurse was on leave that day. The nurse who was posted to the OT in her place was a young girl of twenty-two. She was a greenhorn, just out of nursing school but smart and good at her work.

Before starting an operation, the nurse in charge usually counts the cotton mops. A mop is a piece of sterilized cotton gauze. At the end of the operation, she counts the used and unused mops and totals them. This figure should tally with the number of mops counted at the start of the surgery. This procedure is followed strictly to prevent the possibility of a mop getting left behind in a patient's body through oversight.

The operation was successful and the surgeon was about to sew up and close the abdomen. In keeping with the routine, he asked the OT nurse, 'Sister, is the mop count okay? If it is fine, give me the needle and catgut.'

The young nurse counted the mops and said, 'Sorry doctor, the count is not okay. There is a difference of one mop.'

The surgeon started searching inside the abdomen. He found no mop. 'No, sister, there's nothing inside,' he told her. The nurse searched the OT, but she too could not find the missing mop.

She was quite concerned. If the mop count did not tally, the surgeon could not stitch up the patient's abdomen. The surgeon was concerned too. He insisted that if the missing mop was not found, then there must have been an error in the initial count. But the sister was very confident of her count and was quite firm that she had not gone wrong.

The surgeon became impatient and said, 'Let's not waste any more time. Give me the needle and catgut.'

But the sister would not agree. Politely, but firmly, she said, 'No sir, unless I find that missing mop, I cannot give you the needle and catgut.'

The surgeon contained his rising anger and searched the abdomen once again. Finally, he said in a sharp voice, 'I am the senior person here. I am also responsible. Now, I order you to give me the needle and catgut.'

The nurse was in a dilemma. But she did not change her stance.

The surgeon was really angry by now. 'If you do not obey my instructions, I will dismiss you after the operation,' he warned.

Now the nurse was worried. She was the eldest in her family and the only earning member. It would be terrible if she were to lose her job. She was fully aware of her precarious position, but still she stuck to what she thought was correct. 'Sorry sir, I cannot give you the needle and catgut.'

It was an impossible situation. The inexperienced nurse's apparent defiance had the surgeon fuming. He was so upset that he did not know what to do. He looked down in frustration. To his amazement, he saw the blood-soaked cotton mop lying on the OT floor like a wounded soldier on the battlefield.

He was so relieved that the problem had been sorted out. 'Hey, the mop is here,' he exclaimed. 'Now the count is complete. Give me the—' Before he could complete the sentence, the needle and catgut were in his hands.

After everything was over, the surgeon called the young nurse aside and expressed his appreciation. He told her, 'I am sorry that I put extra pressure on you, sister. However, I am curious to know whether you were scared when I threatened to dismiss you. Did you not believe me when I told you that I was responsible for what happened? Under all this pressure, how could you stand your ground?'

She said hesitantly, 'Sir, I merely obeyed the principle taught to me by my teacher—if the mop count is not correct, then the needle and catgut should not be given to the surgeon. When experienced teachers say something then they must have their reasons. I just followed my teacher's words.'

The surgeon was wonderstruck and immensely pleased.

At the end of a story, my father would say, 'Each patient is precious. Be careful. If a patient dies, it is just one more hospital death for the doctor. But for the unfortunate family, it is a permanent loss.'

6

An Old Man's Ageless Wisdom

Orissa is a state with beautiful thick forests and the famous Chilka Lake. It is well known for its great temples. The Puri Jagannath Temple and the Sun Temple of Konark are among the most remarkable architectural achievements of ancient India. There is also a lot of poverty in Orissa, and around 13,500 NGOs work there to help the poorest of the poor. Many tribal people dwell in remote, inaccessible areas deep in the interior of the state's dense forests. I firmly believe that wherever our company opens a development centre, the services of our Infosys Foundation should also be made available there. Thus Orissa became an area of activity for the Foundation.

Once I had to travel to Kalahandi. It is neither a town nor a city, and it is not known for anything special. It is just another part of another tribal district like Mayur Bhunj or Koraput. They say that before Independence, Kalahandi was ruled by a king. The tribals believed that the king was their caretaker and possessed supreme powers. They are so innocent that, even today, they don't believe that kings no longer exist. If a child is orphaned, it is left at the doorstep of the collector's house. For them the ultimate protector is the raja.

Bhavani Pattanam is the district headquarters of

Kalahandi. It is a small town, quite different from other district headquarters that I know, such as Dharwad, which is my hometown. Frankly, I was surprised that Bhavani Pattanam was such a sleepy place. I had gone there to meet the head of an NGO who had been working tirelessly for the welfare of orphans. Each grey hair on his head told the story of his selfless dedication. In order to serve these children without any distraction, he had chosen to remain unmarried.

While travelling from Bhubaneswar to Kesina, the nearest station, I kept observing the tribal people. They would wait quietly on the platform for their train to arrive. They carried different kinds of fresh produce, such as pineapples, forest bananas and potatoes. The women wore brightly coloured saris—leaf green, bright yellow, dark red—and simply knotted their jet-black hair with flowers tucked in.

I was accompanied by a person who knew the local language and had agreed to be my interpreter. Knowledge of the local language is most essential when one wants to work at the grass-roots level. I had a thousand questions to ask about these tribal people—what civilization meant to them, what their lifestyle was, and so on. Tribals normally live in groups, I was told. They are not too rigid about rituals like we 'civilized' people are. They are direct in their ways. Most importantly, the concept of individual ownership of property is rarely found among them. I was keen to get to know these people. My mission was to provide assistance to them by some means, without threatening their identity.

My interpreter told me that to meet these tribals, I would have to walk two miles, since no car could reach their hamlet. After a long walk, we finally reached a village. I met a woman whose age I could not guess immediately. My interpreter was finding it difficult to translate the lady's words because her dialect was quite different. She was a dark-skinned and dark-haired woman. She must have been around seventy years old but there was no grey in her hair. She obviously could not afford to dye her hair. So what was her secret? The interpreter did not know. But clearly this secret was shared by the entire tribe, because not a single person in that village had a trace of grey hair.

Next, I met an old man. I say old, but again it was virtually impossible to guess his age by simply looking at him. During our conversation, he recalled certain events and occasions and from that we concluded that he was about 104 years old.

I got into a lively conversation with this gentleman. I asked him, 'Who is ruling our country?'

For him 'country' clearly meant Kalahandi. He looked at me and smiled at my ignorance. 'Don't you know?' he said. 'It is company *sarcar* that is ruling our country.' He meant of course the East India Company. The old man was not aware that India had become independent.

I showed him some Indian currency and the emblem of the Ashoka Chakra.

He was not impressed. He said, 'This is just a piece of paper. How can you look at it and tell who is ruling us? It is *goriwali rani* who is ruling us.'

Nothing I said could convince him that the *goriwali rani,* or the 'fair queen' of England, no longer ruled India.

I knew that the barter system was very important to tribal people, so I asked him about that. 'Do you know this small piece of paper can buy firewood, lots of saris, bags of salt, matchsticks, and even a piece of land?'

He looked at me sympathetically and said, 'For this paper, people fight, go away from our ancestral land, leave our forest and go to cities. Have we not led a complete life without that piece of paper? Our ancestors did. We are children of God, settled here happily without this paper. This is God's land. Nobody owns this land. No river is created by us. No mountain is made by us. The wind does not listen to us. The rain does not ask our permission. These are gifts of God. How we can "sell" or "buy" land, I do not understand. When nothing is yours, then how can you make such transactions? This little paper of yours can turn our lives upside down.'

I could find no words to answer him. Until that moment, I had been convinced that I knew more than he did. We know about currency movements, political parties, about the difference between Bill Gates and Bill Clinton. Here was a man who knew nothing of these, yet he was aware of deeper, more eternal truths. He knew that nobody owned the land, the mountains or the wind.

Who is more civilized—this wise old man in the Kalahandi forest or those of us with our fingers on the pulse of the Internet?

7

In India, the Worst of Both Worlds

Monday is the first working day of the week and an extremely busy day in our offices. All emails and papers have to be processed and meetings held. Long lists of appointments inevitably fill up our diaries. In between appointments, unexpected callers invariably turn up. Secretaries sweat it out on Monday mornings. But we have to get past Monday to reach Sunday again.

I recall one such Monday. I was engrossed in checking and replying to my email when my secretary told me that there were two visitors who had come to meet me without an appointment.

I asked her, 'What is special about these visitors that you are letting them in without an appointment?' I have great confidence in my staff and their ways of screening visitors.

She replied in a low tone, 'Ma'am, one is a very old man who looks very pale and the other is a middle-aged person. They say it is very urgent and have been waiting for quite some time.'

'Send them in,' I said.

They came in and sat opposite me. The old man seemed more than seventy years old. He was looking weak, tired and worried. He carried a worn-out bag. He was in a pitiable condition. With him was a middle-aged man who also looked somewhat worried.

I came to the point immediately. 'Tell me, what is the matter?'

The old man did not talk but just looked at the younger man.

The middle-aged man said, 'Madam, I saw this old man sitting near a bus stop. It seems he does not have anybody. He wants some shelter. Unfortunately, he does not have any money.'

This middle-aged man wanted to go on with all kinds of explanations. I often come across people who beat around the bush quite unnecessarily. They never tell you what they want directly. As I am used to such things, I often cut them short even at the risk of sounding curt.

'What do you want me to do?' I asked outright.

'I have read a lot about your work. I want you to help this gentleman.'

'Do you have anybody?' I asked the old man.

Tears welled up in his eyes. In a low voice he said, 'No, I do not have anybody.'

'What about your family?'

'No, I do not have anybody.'

'Where were you working before?'

I asked many questions and he gave reasonably satisfactory replies.

I felt bad for the old man. He had no money and nobody to give him a helping hand. It was a sad case. I thought of an old-age home with which we had regular contact. I called this home and told them that I was sending an old man there and that he should be kept there until we decided what we could do for him. The middle-aged man said, 'Do not worry. I will go with him and leave him there. From there, I will go to my office.'

Then they left my office. Soon, I got lost in my world of work, visitors, vouchers, budgets and so on.

Not that I forgot the old man's case. Once in a while I would call the old-age home and enquire about him. They would tell me that he was fine. I never had time to think more about him. I used to send money every month to the old-age home.

One day, I got a call from the caretaker of the home saying that the old man was very sick and that they had admitted him to a hospital. Could I come in the evening?

I went to see the old man at the hospital that evening. He was really unwell. The doctors felt his condition was critical and that he did not have long to live. I thought there might be somebody he wished to see at a time like this. Maybe not his own children, but perhaps a nephew or a sister or brother, at least a friend? Was there anybody we could inform?

I asked him, 'Do you want to see anybody? We will call whomever you want. Do you have anybody's phone number?'

With a trembling hand, he wrote down a number and gave it to me. We called the number and informed the person at the other end that the old man was critical. After some time, a person came to see him. He looked anxious and worried and he went straight to the old man.

I thought I had seen this man before. I tried to jog my

memory but in vain. I just couldn't remember why the old man's visitor seemed so familiar. Perhaps he resembled someone I had met on my travels.

Meanwhile, the doctor came out and told me that the old man had breathed his last. I felt sad. I neither knew him nor had any contact with him. But somehow I felt very sad.

After a few minutes, the visitor came out. He had tears in his eyes. He sat down quietly on a bench. The whole place was quiet and depressing. The caretaker, this visitor and I sat in the visitors' hall waiting for the formalities to be completed.

The visitor asked, 'Where is the bag he had?'

'What bag?'

'This man came to the old-age home carrying a bag,' he said.

My interest quickened. How did the visitor know that there was a bag?

I sent a peon back to the old-age home to fetch the bag. When it arrived, the visitor was eager to open it, but I did not permit him.

'You may not open the bag unless you identify yourself. What is your relationship with this old man? I want to know how you knew about this bag.'

He seemed very upset with my questions. Maybe he didn't like a woman questioning him. In India, men often get upset when women raise questions that are inconvenient for them. They prefer women who do not question what they do. Fortunately, this trend is disappearing slowly.

'It was I who accompanied him and left him at this home,' said the man.

'Who are you?' I was very curious.

'I am his son.'

You can imagine how shocked I was. Now I remembered—he was the middle-aged man who had come to our office that Monday morning claiming that he had found the old man sitting near a bus stop.

I was very upset. 'Why did you lie to me?'

Of course he had a story to tell. 'I have problems at home,' he said. 'My wife never liked my father. She asked me to choose between her and him. At that time we read about your Foundation. We thought then that our problem could be solved without money.' He said he had no choice but to appease his wife because it was she who owned the house they lived in.

'What a way to solve your problem!' I protested. 'We help people who are orphans, but not orphans with children.'

When the bag was finally opened we found three sets of old clothes in it, some medicines and a passbook. When I opened the passbook, I was astounded. The old man had a bank balance of more than a lakh of rupees. The old man had put down a nominee for the account—his son, the same son who had got rid of him. Here was a son who was heartless enough to pass off his father as destitute in order to admit him in an old-age home. Now, the same son had come to claim his father's money.

Though his son had not wanted to look after him and had made him lie to me that he had nobody in this world, the old man nevertheless had wanted his money to go to his son. It never would have occurred to him to give that money to the old-age home that had sheltered him in his last days.

In Western countries, when old people die in old-age homes, they often will their property to the home or the hospital that cared for them. This is for the benefit of other senior citizens. They do not bequeath their money to their children, nor do the children expect their parents to do so. But in India, we have the worst of both worlds: children neglect aged parents, and parents routinely leave their property to their children.

'It is shameful the way you and your father cooked up this drama for the sake of a few thousand rupees!' I told the man. 'And you are setting a bad example. Next time when a genuinely destitute person seeks help, we will be unwilling to offer it. The memory of people like you will stay on.'

He hung his head in shame.

8

LIVING THROUGH CHANGE

Life and times have changed in truly revolutionary ways. Yet, we seldom feel the impact of change because we live right in the middle of it. Old ways have changed, our festivals have changed, our attitudes have changed, our norms, values and ideas have changed. Two festivals in which I participated recently brought this point home to me fairly dramatically. In both cases, the extent of change that had taken place was conveyed to me through conversation. This added a personal touch and helped underline the fundamental nature of the changes through which we are living. The first event was a Diwali celebration. The second was a music festival.

Diwali is an occasion for great celebration in our country. Everybody buys gifts, prepares sweets and visits friends. Offices remain closed for days. Children buy crackers.

Last Diwali, I saw an advertisement saying that some orphanages were selling sweets prepared by the orphans. I thought that buying these sweets would be the best way to help and encourage the orphanages. I bought a few packets of sweets and went to the house of a close friend.

I expected her to be in a joyous mood, celebrating this great festival with enthusiasm. She was a housewife, hailing from a small town. Her father owned plenty of land in the village. Surprisingly, I found her far from joyous. She didn't seem enthusiastic at all about the festival I had gone to celebrate with her.

'Diwali has lost its real meaning,' she said.

I was frankly surprised to hear this. 'Why do you say that?' I asked her.

She had her reasons. 'In the small town I grew up in, our food pattern was so different from what it is today. Everyone used to have healthy but simple food like roti, rice, dal and vegetables every day, irrespective of the family's income. Sweets were prepared only when there was a festival like Dussera or Diwali. That being so, we children looked forward to the festivals.'

My thoughts went back to my own childhood days. They were similar to hers. We used to eat a healthy and balanced diet like she said.

'But nowadays,' she went on, 'food patterns have changed. One reason is that we have only two children and are keen to give them what they like. We cook accordingly. In case we cannot cook what they want, then in a city like ours we can order it instantly from any restaurant. So children today have no reason to look forward to festivals and sweets like we used to.'

Of course she was right. Food habits have indeed changed. This is particularly true of the middle class and the upper middle class. But I still had a question. Was the availability of sweets throughout the year the only reason for people to lose interest in Diwali?

'No,' said my friend, 'the whole attitude has changed.

People buy whatever clothes they want, whenever they want. They don't wait for any festival. Families are scattered all over India, and sometimes all over the world. Meeting one's relatives is not easy. Even amongst my friends, many of them would like to go to their home town. But getting reservations by rail, air or even by bus, has become so difficult that it is better to stay at home.'

How true! For the trip I would take over Diwali, I had booked my tickets a month in advance.

My friend raised the most fundamental issue when she asked, 'How many of us really know the significance of Diwali? The real meaning of the festival of lights? What our sacred epics say about this festival? The reality is that nobody is bothered. In our country, each state has a special story about this festival. All the stories are from parts of the Mahabharatha and the Krishna legend. But how many know about them?'

I thought that perhaps she was feeling homesick. In such a situation, I told myself, the best thing to do would be to take her out of the house.

'Let us go to Renu's house or Mridula's house,' I suggested. They were old friends and therefore real friends. Nowadays many people refer to me as their friend though I may not know them. Renu and Mridula were different and I thought visiting them would cheer up my depressed friend. But she had news for me.

'No, Renu got bored,' my friend said. 'She works as HRD head in a big firm and she is really tired of having to take care of so many visitors during the Diwali season. So, she has gone to Goa for a holiday. And Mridula is writing a book. She told me not to tell anybody that she is in the company guest house.'

This was something new to me—this method of celebrating Diwali by escaping or hibernating.

My friend had not finished. 'There is one more headache. Some relatives bring gifts, so we have to reciprocate. It has become a racket. I did not unpack last year's gifts hoping that I could give them to somebody this year. I am tired of candle stands and boxes of dry fruits and sweets. We are all getting old. Extra calories and cholesterol-rich sweets are not good for us.'

'So what did you do with them?' I asked.

'I gave them to an orphanage. Let the poor children enjoy themselves.'

I was curious to know to whom she had given the sweets. She named a well-known orphanage. Now I knew what happens to the sweets or candles gifted at Diwali! They are labelled in the name of some charitable organization and sold in the market. What a wonderful way to raise funds! Of course, the little children in the orphanages may still not get to eat any sweets on Diwali.

My music festival experience was quite different but equally illuminating. These days, I am often invited to inaugurate music festivals, philosophy lectures or charity shows. Often, I do not know anything about the subject concerned. But people get offended if I refuse. So, I accept these invitations on the condition that I should not be called to the dais.

I attended one such festival recently. I just wanted to enjoy the music. I went late, so I sat at the back, quite happy that nobody had noticed me. There were retired officers, middle-aged housewives and old ladies, but I could not see any youngsters in the hall. Two middle-aged housewives wearing Dharmavaram saris were sitting right in front of me. They looked elegant with fresh jasmine flowers in their silvery hair. Since the rows were close, I couldn't help but hear what they were talking about. They were discussing the problems of finding grooms for girls these days.

'The software boom has made it difficult to get grooms above twenty-eight years these days,' said one woman profoundly.

The other woman was also interested in the topic. Obviously, the subject of grooms was far more important to them than the music.

The first woman went on to explain, 'Today, when a boy completes his BE, he may be twenty-two years, and he will get a job in one of the software companies. He will work for two years and then he will go abroad for a year. By that time he will be twenty-five and probably would have earned more money than his father, who might have been a bank officer, an honest government employee or a professor. Tell me, why should he not marry and settle down?'

Unaware that someone was eavesdropping, she answered her own question. 'His parents will search for a software engineer girl. Today, I've been told that about 50 per cent of the students in engineering colleges are girls. An engineering college is just like an arts college these days. I am sure the boy's father will get a software girl. The marriage is good for both of them in every sense of the word. He will have someone with him when he works abroad. He will have home-cooked food and there will be somebody to look after him. For the girl also it will be such an advantage. So, at twenty-five, these young men will get married—just like in the old days.'

This woman definitely deserves a medal for her logical and accurate analysis, I told myself. Now it was the turn of the other woman to give her views. She had a different perspective.

'This software boom is really bad in some ways,' she said. 'Look at how it affects others. Nowadays, girls say they do not want to marry electrical engineers, mechanical engineers or even doctors. The chances of these boys going abroad are limited. Their salaries are also not very attractive. Most important of all, they are not respected in the family.'

I was really surprised by this last statement and was eager to hear an explanation for it. I was not disappointed.

'If the boy is abroad,' the lady continued, 'then he will come home for three weeks, bringing gifts with him. Everybody likes him for that. But engineers or doctors don't get the same opportunities to work abroad. Also, if the daughter-in-law stays with her mother-in-law all the time, she is not respected. Today, no girl likes to stay with her mother-in-law. Going abroad is the best solution, but this must be immediately after marriage, not later.'

'Why not later?'

'Later, it is better to be with the in-laws. There will be children and the in-laws will look after them. There will be nothing to worry about. No need to depend on servants. This kind of shuttling between India and the US is possible only in a software job.'

I could not control myself any longer. A whole new window had opened before my eyes and I wanted to know who these women were. They had come to such a beautiful music concert, but preferred to exchange notes on the social aspects of software development. I knew it was bad manners, but I couldn't help interrupting their conversation. 'Excuse me,' I said, 'I am curious to know how you both know so much about software sociology.'

They were startled and turned around to stare at me. I felt that they did not like my question. And I could not blame them. After all, I had broken into what was a private conversation.

'Who are you?' they asked.

I introduced myself and said, 'I have known the software industry for the last two decades but I did not know these social details. I must really compliment both of you on your knowledge.'

My compliment seemed to put them at ease for they smiled as they replied together, 'We are marriage brokers.'

9

When Telegrams Were Bad

The difference between animals and human beings is communication. If one is good at it, then many misunderstandings can be reduced. Clear thinking and clear communication are therefore essential in everyday life. Indeed, many communication classes are offered nowadays. For those in a hurry, there are crash courses.

Lata and I were close friends right from childhood. In a small town, friendship grows faster and thicker than in big cities. Maybe people from small towns depend on each other more. Or maybe the culture in a small place is different than in a big city. Industrialization has its own impact on human relations. In our small-town environment, Lata and I enjoyed our closeness. I was a frequent visitor to her house and I knew everybody there. It was the same with Lata. She came over to our place often and knew my family very well. In due course, we completed our degrees and the time came for us to go our different ways. We parted with heavy hearts as I took up a job in Pune and went away.

I became involved in my career and used to meet Lata only when I visited my home town. Telephones were the prerogative of the rich in those days—I am talking of the situation some twenty-five years ago—and roadside STD booths were unknown. If anything was urgent, the only channel of communication available was the telegram. The telegram denoted a whole new culture in those days. In villages and small towns, a telegram was a big event, often a harbinger of bad news.

One day, I received a telegram. As usual, it was ominous. 'Father expired. Start immediately,' it said. The sender's name was given as Lata.

I was shocked. My colleagues were very kind to me. One of them called the railway station immediately to book a ticket on the next train to my home town while another applied for leave on my behalf. I just sat still, crying.

My father was more than a friend to me. We used to talk a lot and discuss many things. The previous week, when I had visited him, he had been hale and hearty. He had not shown any signs of illness. What could have happened? Was it a heart attack or an accident? How was my mother? How difficult it would be for her!

One of my colleagues used to get a telegram similar to the one I had just received at least once every year. 'Granny expired. Start immediately,' his telegram would read. He would tell me that this was the best way to get leave.

'Do you have enough leave?' he asked me now, thinking the telegram I had received was one like his. I was very angry with him.

My journey back home was simply unbearable. I thought of my childhood and my college days when my father was a part of everything. At first he was a role model, but later, when I had seen more of the world, he became more of a friend than a hero.

I remember feeling that my childhood had gone forever. My father and I had so many dreams of travelling together, reading many books and discussing things. All my dreams were shattered. I knew life had to go on, but I thought that if he were alive then life would have been so much more enjoyable.

When I reached my home town, I was expecting at least one of my numerous cousins to be at the station to receive me. To my surprise, there was no one from my family. I was a little upset. Then I consoled myself thinking that everybody must be in mourning. And anyhow, how were they to know that I was coming by this particular train, I reasoned. So I took an auto and reached home. As we neared the house, my heart started pounding—the same road, the same house, but today it was without my dear father.

I got down from the auto and noticed that the house was rather quiet. It was calm and there was no sign of people inside. I was surprised. How could that be? My father was a very popular doctor and professor. Surely people would have come to pay their last respects. I couldn't see any of my cousins either. I went in. The house was whitewashed, decorated with flowers and mango leaves. It looked as though it was a happy occasion. I did not know what to do. I stood there still and silent, like a lamp post.

Just then there was a noise coming from my father's room. I turned and I could not believe what I saw. My father was standing there, smiling happily at me. Is it a dream? I asked myself.

My father seemed very happy to see me. He said, 'I knew that you would make it for the engagement somehow. She is your favourite cousin after all.'

'What are you talking about?'

'The engagement. Lata's marriage is fixed. The boy's family wants to hold the engagement this evening itself. He is in Delhi. The marriage is . . .'

I stopped him. 'Who sent the telegram? Why did you write that? Why did you lie to me? You of all people! I never expected you to lie.'

But my father did not understand what I was saying. 'What telegram are you talking about? We had to send a telegram so that you could come.'

'But why this kind of telegram?' I was very upset and agitated as I gave him the telegram I had received. My father was surprised and said that he hadn't sent it. Confusion. Then who had sent it?

Suddenly, he smiled. 'I know what must have happened. Your friend Lata's father passed away yesterday. You know that he was sick. You knew him very well. That may be the reason why Lata sent you a telegram. There was a miscommunication. She should have said, "*My* father passed away".' The word 'my' was missing. What havoc it had caused!

It was now clear to me that the telegram was sent by my friend Lata, and back home it was celebration time for my cousin Lata's engagement. I was left wondering what my colleagues would think when they saw the other telegram, the one actually sent by my family, which read, 'Lata's marriage fixed. Engagement tomorrow.'

10

A Man Too Clever by Half

A few years ago, when the Infosys Foundation was still in its infancy, people were not aware of the kind of work we were trying to do. Our organization worked at the grass-roots level, mainly with village schoolmasters whom we approached voluntarily. Although Infosys, the company, had already made a name for itself in the field of business, the Foundation was housed in two small rooms on the third floor of Infosys Towers; and it still is, even today. Our obscurity was heightened by the fact that there wasn't a single plaque announcing our presence. The security men would confront our staff frequently. Any decent establishment connected to Infosys should have a large signboard with brass lettering, if not a stately banner, they would say.

Right from its inception, the Foundation focused on redressing the grievances of village people, especially children, so that we could help them envision a bright and prosperous future comparable to that of their urban counterparts. It is well known that in our country the rural-urban divide runs deep. The life of village children is devoid of the activities that are taken for granted by our city children. The simple pleasures of modern life—watching a cartoon show on television, listening to a popular Hindi film song, or even reading a book at leisure—are rare luxuries in villages. A lack of basic facilities forces village boys and girls to while away their time uselessly. Having observed this aspect of village life at close quarters, I decided that one of the primary goals of the Foundation should be to launch a project titled 'A library for each village'.

I feel libraries play an important role in the lives of children, the citizens of tomorrow. As I was raised in a middle-class family in a small town, I was well aware of the importance of books and knowledge in the life of a student. In my childhood, I had limited access to books and it was then that I had envisioned starting free libraries offering unlimited access to the world of books. As soon as I had been named trustee of the Foundation, I knew I had to take the first step towards fulfilling my desire to build libraries for village children.

Reading has many advantages. It is not only a useful hobby, but also helps us imbibe better qualities. Keeping this in mind, the trustees planned to establish libraries that contained books in the regional language and not the textbooks that the children were using in school. Simple, illustrated, interesting books that could be read without anybody's help were thus selected for these libraries. In this manner, the Foundation would sow the seeds of a love for reading in the villages of Karnataka.

With sufficient nurturing and caring, the project has grown from a tiny sapling into a huge, wide-reaching banyan tree. More than 4,000 such libraries have been established all over the state. The books have succeeded in putting a smile on the faces of village children who discovered a new world opening up before them.

One hot afternoon, when I was sitting in my room trying to come up with some innovative ideas for the Foundation's projects, I noticed the silhouette of a man standing outside the glass door of my office. He was barely visible among the cartons of books and the jungle of colourful wrapping paper strewn all over the floor. I carried on with my work, which required concentration. It was one of those days when my eagerness to complete the work on hand had made me give up all thoughts of a quick lunch or a midday siesta. Suddenly, I was startled by a loud knock on the door. The stranger walked in, without even a nominal 'May I come in?'

'Is this the Foundation office?' he asked abruptly.

'Yes,' I answered.

'Are you one of the staff members of the Foundation?'

I nodded. He looked puzzled. Perhaps he had expected to see a fancy office with a fancy receptionist. And here was I, wearing the sort of simple cotton sari that did nothing to disclose my identity. When the man arrived, I had been engrossed in dispatching some last-minute packages while also writing an introductory proposal for a new project. A dishevelled person in a tiny cabin amid a maze of paper and piles of books was clearly not his idea of the Infosys Foundation he had come to visit. Without wasting time on introductions, he opened his bag and pulled out two Kannada books that looked like pamphlets.

'These are very good books for children,' he announced. 'I have put in several years and the best of my efforts to publish them. There is a great demand for these books all over Karnataka. You can buy these books for your library project.'

I just listened. Naturally, I wanted to see the books for myself to judge their quality, price and, most importantly, content. Would they prove useful and interesting to children in village schools?

My silence seemed to irritate him. He said, 'I know Sudha Murty and Narayana Murthy very well. Mrs Murty, who is the trustee of the Foundation, asked me to come here. Otherwise I don't do this kind of a salesman's job. It is because of the rapport we share that I have come so far to help her.'

I was amused. 'Have you known Mrs Murty for many years?' I asked.

Without any hesitation, he answered, 'I've known Sudha for a long time. She is my childhood friend.'

This was getting more and more curious—a man I was seeing for the first time claiming to be my childhood friend!

Rather naughtily, I asked, 'But Sudha is from Dharwad and you seem to be from Bangalore. How is it that she is your childhood friend?'

Now he looked quite surprised. 'Do you address your boss by her first name? It is not good etiquette. So what if she is from Dharwad? She used to come to Bangalore quite often to her aunt's house, which is next to ours even now.'

Lord Almighty, I thought. My kith and kin had never crossed the Tungabhadra River, which divides the old Mysore state from northern Karnataka. So, I was indeed surprised to know about this 'aunt' who was his neighbour.

He went on, 'Sudha has always treated me like her elder brother. She doesn't have any brothers, you see. When Murthy wanted to start Infosys, she came to me for advice. Recently she told me she wanted to buy 100 copies of each of my books. She knows my calibre. She told me to give these books here and collect the money. I have to go to the Kannada Sahitya meeting where they are honouring me, so please hurry up.'

I didn't know whether to get upset and shout at him or just carry on with the ruse. I decided to play along with his deception. 'What kind of a person is Mrs Murty?' I asked, perhaps impishly.

He seemed pleased at the opportunity to say more about his friendship. 'Oh! She is a gentle lady, though very quiet by nature,' he said. 'During her MA, nobody even knew about Sudha in the class. It was I who told her not to waste her time at home and do some social work. I also introduced her to Murthy and mediated their marriage.'

'Was it an arranged marriage?'

'Of course. I even got their horoscopes matched. That's why the couple is very fond of me even now and hold me in high regard. After all, it's because of me that she is here today!'

This was too much. He was not even being clever, just careless. Mine was a love marriage. Neither of us was bothered about horoscopes. Moreover, I have always been an extrovert and was much noticed because I happened to be the only girl in class throughout my college days. I am an M.Tech and not an MA. Social service was a cherished idea of Murthy's and mine since the days of our friendship.

I could no longer stand this man's lying. I realized it was time to call his bluff. If I didn't disclose my identity now, who knew what he would be claiming next.

'Mister,' I said very sternly, 'there has to be an end to these lies of yours. I am Sudha Murty, wife of Narayana Murthy. This is the first time that I am meeting you. How dare you talk about Murthy and me in this way? This is outrageous! Even if your books were good in terms of content and language, I would never buy them. Books are meant to reflect the thoughts and personality of the author. By now I know what kind of a person you are. Even if you are willing to offer your books free, I shall not accept them. Remember, only an honest human being can be a good writer.'

He was shocked of course. But before he could think of a suitable response, I had walked out of the office, disgusted, frustrated and amazed at the world we live in.

11

A Bond Betrayed on Rakhi Day

My work at the Infosys Foundation has brought me face to face with many women who have suffered a great deal for no fault of theirs. Most of them are uneducated and victims of exploitation. One of the objectives of our Foundation is to try and help these unlucky women as much as possible.

Those who slip into prostitution are almost always innocent women. Most have been forced into it at a young age and they find it difficult to escape. Many express a desire to leave the profession, but that is next to impossible. Since they have been in this 'trade' from a young age, they have not developed any other special skills. Hence they are not fit for employment and are unable to find alternative means of earning a livelihood. In those rare cases when a woman does manage to extricate herself from this miserable life, our society does not accept her.

In the last few years, I have had some experience in working for these unfortunate women. Initially, they would avoid talking to me. But on repeated visits, they opened up gradually and started speaking with me. The stories they narrated were heartbreaking. At times, I was really at a loss for what to say or how to react. Their agony pained me deeply.

It was on one such visit that I got to know Tara, a middle-aged *gharwali* (commercial sex worker) in a temple. Looking at Tara, I could tell that she had been a very beautiful woman in her younger days. Even now, she came across as someone who was bold and spirited. Tara did not know how to read and write and wanted my help because she thought I was a school teacher. That was fine with me.

'If you know of any other lady teacher, please let me know. I want to learn to read and write,' she told me the first time we met. 'I don't want to call her to my house. I will go wherever the teacher wants me to.'

Her zest for knowledge surprised me. I wanted to know more about her. Once or twice, I tried to broach the subject, but she was reluctant to talk about herself. She always seemed very sad.

It was Rakhi day. In northern Karnataka and the border areas of Maharashtra, this day is called Narali-Poornima, which literally means 'to celebrate the full-moon day with coconuts'. I was in the area for a week, mainly visiting village schools in connection with our library project. There I bumped into Tara again. I still remember it was a bright, sunny day and Tara was buying bangles. I wanted to talk to her. How should I address her, I wondered. Since she was older than me, I decided to call her akka, which means elder sister in Kannada.

Tara was sitting on the steps of the temple, waiting for the crowd to disperse. I went towards her. She looked at me and smiled. I thought she was sad. Or was I sad? I didn't know.

I tried to begin a conversation by returning her smile. 'Tara akka, there is such a crowd because of Narali-Poornima. You will have to wait for a long time to get in.'

Suddenly, I sensed anger. I could see it in her eyes. She began to shout at me. 'Teacher, don't call me akka. I dislike that word. All these relationships, like brother and sister, exist in your world. Not in mine. Don't address me like that. You can call me Tara, Tarabai, but not Tara akka. In my world there is only one relationship, that of a man and a woman.'

Tears rolled down my eyes. I understood the bitter truth behind what she said. One of the volunteers who had accompanied me was very upset. He wanted to tell Tara who I was. I stopped him.

'Tara, I am sorry if I hurt your feelings,' I said politely. 'I used the word akka because you are older than me. I'm sorry if that offended you.'

The atmosphere then changed dramatically. Tara started crying uncontrollably. The pallu of her green Irkal sari became wet with tears. Holding the bangles she had bought from the shop in one hand, she used the other to wipe her tears.

I put my hand on her shoulder. I did not speak. Our silence was much more meaningful than words. After some time, she stopped crying, but she still looked very sad. I sent my volunteer to fetch a cup of tea for her. After a while, Tara calmed down.

She said, 'Teacher, I am sorry I was rude to you. You have not made any mistake. After all, you have shown respect to me by calling me akka. Till this day, no one has ever used such a good word to address me. People call me by different names. I don't want to repeat them to you. Akka brought back childhood memories.'

Tara continued talking. She spoke of her poverty and of losing her parents in an epidemic. A younger brother was all she had. She adored him and though she was only a child herself she found work as a coolie to look after him. But when she was twelve years old and her brother was only eleven, he sold her to an agent in a red light area. He had taken her there on the pretext of visiting the village fair. That was on a Narali-Poornima day.

It was now clear to me what she was going through sitting on the steps of that temple. It was Narali-Poornima day once again and the word akka must have triggered in her mind something she had been desperate to forget all her life. Rakhi is not merely about a sister tying a thread on her brother's wrist. It signifies the bond between a brother and a sister. And Tara, through no fault of hers, was pushed into her dreadful life by her own brother. On a Rakhi day.

12

A Lesson in Life from a Beggar

Meena is a good friend of mine. She is an LIC officer earning a good salary. But there was always something strange about her. She was forever unhappy. Whenever I met her, I would start to feel depressed. It was as though her gloom and cynicism had a way of spreading to others. She never had anything positive to say on any subject or about any person.

For instance, I might say to her, 'Meena, did you know Rakesh has come first in his school?'

Meena's immediate response would be to belittle the achievement. 'Naturally, his father is a school teacher,' she would say.

If I said, 'Meena, Shwetha is a very beautiful girl, isn't she?' Meena would be pessimistic. 'When a pony is young, he looks handsome. It is age that matters. Wait for some time. Shwetha will be uglier than anyone you know.'

'Meena, it's a beautiful day. Let's go for a walk.'

'No, the sun is too hot and I get tired if I walk too much. Besides, who says walking is good for health? There's no proof.'

That was Meena. She stayed alone in an apartment as her parents lived in Delhi. She was an only child and had the habit of complaining about anything and everything.

Naturally, she wasn't very pleasant company and nobody wanted to visit her. Then one day, Meena was transferred to Bombay and soon we all forgot about her.

Many years later, I found myself caught in the rain at Bombay's Flora Fountain. It was pouring and I didn't have an umbrella. I was standing near Akbarallys, a popular department store, waiting for the rain to subside. Suddenly, I spotted Meena. My first reaction was to run, even in that pouring rain. I was anxious to avoid being seen by her, having to listen to her never-ending complaints. However, I couldn't escape. She had already seen me and caught hold of my hand warmly. What's more, she was very cheerful.

'Hey! I am really excited. It's nice to meet old friends. What are you doing here?'

I explained that I was in Bombay on official work.

'Then stay with me tonight,' she said. 'Let's chat. Do you know that old wine, old friends and memories are precious and rare?'

I couldn't believe it. Was this really Meena? I pinched myself hard to be sure it wasn't a dream. But Meena was really standing there, right in front of me, squeezing my hand, smiling, and yes, she did look happy. In the three years she had been in Bangalore, I had never once seen her smiling like that. A few strands of grey in her hair reminded me that years had passed. There were a few wrinkles in her face, but the truth was that she looked more attractive than ever before.

Finally, I managed to say, 'No Meena, I can't stay with you tonight. I have to attend a dinner. Give me your card and I'll keep in touch with you. I promise.'

For a moment, Meena looked disappointed. 'Let's go and have tea at least,' she insisted.

'But Meena, it's pouring.'

'So what? We'll buy an umbrella and then go to the Grand Hotel,' she said.

'We won't get a taxi in this rain,' I grumbled.

'So what? We'll walk.'

I was very surprised. This wasn't the same Meena I had known. Today, she seemed ready to make any number of adjustments.

We reached the Grand Hotel drenched. By then the only thought in my mind was to find out who or what had brought about such a change in the pessimistic Meena I had known. I was quite curious.

'Tell me Meena, is there a Prince Charming who has managed to change you so?'

Meena was surprised by my question. 'No, there isn't anyone like that,' she said.

'Then what's the secret of your energy?' I asked, like Tendulkar does in the ad.

She smiled. 'A beggar changed my life.'

I was absolutely dumbfounded and she could see it.

'Yes, a beggar,' she repeated, as if to reassure me. 'He was old and used to stay in front of my house with his five-year-old granddaughter. As you know, I was a chronic pessimist. I used to give my leftovers to this beggar every day. I never spoke to him. Nor did he speak to me. One monsoon day, I looked out of my bedroom window and started cursing the rain. I don't know why I did that because I wasn't even getting wet. That day I couldn't give the beggar and his granddaughter their daily quota of leftovers. They went hungry, I am sure.

'However, what I saw from my window surprised me. The beggar and the young girl were playing on the road because there was no traffic. They were laughing, clapping and screaming joyously, as if they were in paradise. Hunger and rain did not matter. They were totally drenched and totally happy. I envied their zest for life.

'That scene forced me to look at my own life. I realized I had so many comforts, none of which they had. But they had the most important of all assets, one which I lacked. They knew how to be happy with life as it was. I felt ashamed of myself. I even started to make a list of what I had and what I did not have. I found I had more to be grateful for than most people could imagine. That day, I decided to change my attitude towards life, using the beggar as my role model.'

After a long pause, I asked Meena how long it had taken her to change.

'Once this realization dawned,' she said, 'it took me almost two years to put the change into effect. Now nothing matters. I am always happy. I find happiness in every small thing, in every situation and in every person.'

'Did you give any *gurudakshina* to your guru?' I asked.

'No. Unfortunately, by the time I understood things, he was dead. But I sponsored his granddaughter to a boarding school as a mark of respect to him.'

13

FORGETTING OUR OWN HISTORY

Our country's history is full of martyrs and patriots in whose honour we must bow our heads in perpetual tribute. Their life stories are gloriously inspirational. Particularly inspiring are the stories of our women martyrs. Many of them were not even educated, but they had the courage to face their enemies and fight for their country. Obvavva of Chitradurga district, Kittur Chennamma of northern Karnataka, Belavadi Maamma of Belgaum district—the list is long. Obvavva had nothing but the rice-pounding stick from her kitchen to use against the fully armed enemy soldiers. But how many of our young Indians know about them?

Among history's heroines, few shine as brightly as Rani Laxmibai of Jhansi. A young childless widow, she challenged the might of the British Empire. Such was her courage that she won the admiration of even the enemy. There are many poems written about her. The greatest compliment paid to her courage was the saying that she was the only man in her army. How much do our young people know about her?

Recently, I received the Ojaswini Award from Bhopal. It was presented to me in Delhi. It included a beautiful memento—a statue of Rani Laxmibai of Jhansi riding a horse, sword in hand. It was exquisitely crafted. I returned to Bangalore by air and carried the statue, though rather large, as hand baggage. I feared that it would break if I checked it in. The security personnel at Delhi airport were very kind to me after I explained my situation. They scanned the statue with metal detectors and allowed me to carry it into the aircraft.

The Jet Airways crew were equally nice. I was in economy class and could not keep the statue on my lap. I didn't want to put it under the seat either. Of course, it wouldn't fit into the overhead locker. The air hostess very kindly took away my statue and placed it on an empty seat in business class. Without a doubt, Mardani Rani Laxmibai deserved this deferential treatment.

Quite pleased with the way everyone had helped, I settled down comfortably. I noticed that my fellow passengers were watching these goings-on with interest. After the flight took off, they looked at me with curious eyes. But no one ventured to strike up a conversation.

I have a theory about conversation. You may call it an empirical formula. Quantitatively speaking, 'conversation' is inversely proportional to economic standing. If you are travelling by bus, your fellow passengers will get into conversation with you very quickly and without any reservation. If you are travelling by first class on a train, people will be more reserved. If you are travelling by air, then the likelihood of entering into a conversation is quite small. If you are in first class on an international flight, then you may travel twenty-four hours without exchanging a single word with the person sitting next to you.

There were two teenagers sitting next to me on the Delhi-Bangalore flight, a boy and a girl. They were wearing expensive branded jeans. Both had cut their hair short, making them look similar. The only noticeable difference was that the girl had pierced her ears. They were chewing gum and an MP3 player kept them immersed in their own world. It was evident that they were from an affluent family. It was just as evident that they were in no mood for conversation, even among themselves, let alone others. Music and gum do that to people.

After some time, I decided that I must break the ice and talk to these youngsters. As I teach in a college, I am comfortable with young people. I enjoy talking to them. Normally, at that age they are not manipulative or shrewd. They are spontaneous and less inhibited and often have refreshing views. I engaged them first in small talk and found out that they were studying in a college in Bangalore. They were cousins and had just been to Delhi to visit their grandparents.

The girl asked hesitantly, 'I saw that statue of a black horse and a woman riding on it. It's a nice toy, but is it not available in Bangalore? You seem to have had such a tough time carrying it with you. Is there any special reason for carrying it with you?'

'It's not a toy. It's an award,' I told her.

Now the boy started to ply me with questions. 'Are you very fond of horses?'

I was surprised. 'No, I hardly see horses nowadays.'

'Maybe you are fond of the races!'

I have never gone to a race in my life. I felt a bit uncomfortable. It was getting dark as it was an evening flight, so the young cousins did not see the frown on my face.

The boy asked, 'Is this award for a horse race? There is a lady on the back of that beautiful horse.'

I realized that these young people could only associate my trophy with horses and races. They had absolutely no idea about the woman in battle gear sitting astride the horse. Was I being given an opportunity to tell them?

'Will you go and have a look at the statue and tell me what you think about it?' I asked them.

'We did look at the statue and that's why we are asking these questions,' they replied.

I was taken aback. Being a teacher, I thought it was my duty to tell them about Rani Laxmibai. (I now realize why my son teases me about my habit of viewing every youngster as a potential student and my eagerness to convert every moment available into an opportunity for teaching.)

'Have you heard about the First War of Independence?' I asked the youngsters.

'Yes. It was in 1942, wasn't it?' said the boy vaguely.

The girl added, 'Of course, we've seen the movie *1942– A Love Story*. The war between the Indians and the British. Manisha Koirala was just stunning in that.'

'No, that was the Quit India movement. The First War of Independence was fought a century before that and we lost it.'

They did not reply.

'In 1857 there was a war against the British. The young queen of Jhansi, Rani Laxmibai, led her forces against them. She could have remained passive, accepted a royal pension from the British and led a secure, comfortable life. But she didn't do that. She was a fiery patriot. She fought the war bravely and even her opponents were surprised by her leadership on the battlefield. Since then she has been a symbol of courage and an icon of the Indian people's love of freedom. She died so that we could all live in a free India.'

The two youngsters listened without saying a word. And without chewing.

Travelling opens the doors to knowledge. Without it, education is incomplete. Our country is special in so many ways. It has many states, each with a different language, traditions, customs, flora and fauna. Travelling within India itself gives you the feel and the pleasure of visiting different countries.

If you travel by bus or by second class in a train, then you'll meet people from different backgrounds. It is particularly pleasurable to converse with one's fellow passengers on a bus or a train. I discover this often—like the time I was travelling from Bangalore to Hubli by a day train. Normally in such trains we don't require reservations. We can enjoy the view of nature and also have the pleasure of meeting various kinds of people.

I boarded the train at 2.30 p.m. in Bangalore and was supposed to reach Hubli by 10 p.m. I was alone and was tired after having worked almost continuously on a project for the previous two days. Rest was what I needed most at that time.

I occupied a window seat, stretched my legs and settled down to doze. Just then, someone entered the compartment and sat down beside me. It was a young woman, about twenty-five years old, dressed in a cotton sari. Probably she had come at the eleventh hour and had to run to catch the train, for she was perspiring. She wore no ornaments or any other adornment. She was evidently from an average middle-class family.

She settled down, took out a handkerchief and started wiping her face, looking into the mirror attached to her purse. She drank some water and then looked at me. She reminded me of an enthusiastic, well-prepared student going for an examination. She smiled at me in a friendly way. She seemed ready to start a conversation.

The inevitable opening question came first. 'Where are you going?'

'Hubli,' I said

'Where in Hubli?'

I was hesitant to give her any details, but I found myself replying, 'Vishweshwaranagar. Do you know where that is?'

'Sort of,' she said casually.

'I am going to the Shanti Colony.'

'Where in Shanti Colony?' she wanted to know. 'Because there are two Shanti Colonies.'

I was taken aback by her knowledge of the area. 'Near the railway lines.'

'Both are near railway lines. Is it north or south?'

'North,' I clarified.

I thought I had satisfied her curiosity and that there would be no further questions. Now I looked forward to some rest. I am by nature a friendly and outgoing person, and I love talking to different people, but in the train that day I was tired and wasn't in the mood for conversation.

But the girl did not think the conversation was over.

'Do you work?' she began again.

Expecting further probing, I decided to give her all the details right away. 'Yes, I work in a college and now I have holidays. I belong to Hubli so I am going there.'

If I thought that would satisfy her, I was mistaken. She smiled and said, 'Oh, I see! So you are a professor. What subjects do you teach?'

People who are fond of talking can raise a conversation out of nothing. Introverts, on the other hand, can answer in monosyllables and end a conversation quickly. Some people use conversation to gather a great deal of information about others without divulging any information about themselves. I realized that this young woman belonged to such a category. My sleep and irritation disappeared. I decided to play this game and find out how many questions she could generate.

'I teach computer science at Christ College.'

'Oh, computers! There is no place without a computer nowadays. A day may come when we might be called illiterate if we do not know computers. What do you say?'

I had begun to appreciate her ability to invent questions and pull me into the conversation.

'It depends on how you interpret the concept of literacy,' I answered like a management consultant.

She responded with a comment, 'I strongly believe that there is a great difference between being literate and being educated. Literacy means having the basic knowledge, being educated means understanding what you know. What do you think about this definition?'

I was in a fix to understand this woman. By this time, the train had crossed Bangalore city limits and was heading towards Tumkur. I could see the beautiful landscape passing by. It was just after the monsoon, so the lakes were full and the land was green. The weather was pleasant and no air conditioning or fans were required. Men and women were working in the fields. Cattle were grazing. Hills loomed majestically against the sky. Though it was late afternoon, the sun was not hot.

I thought that if this lady were to go on talking, then it would be impossible to bear the six to seven hours that were left of my journey. One way to save the situation was to tell her politely but firmly that I wanted to rest and would prefer to be left alone. But somehow I was unable to be frank with her. She looked so innocent. She was bubbling with energy. Her face had an open and curious expression. She looked just like one of my eager students in class. As a teacher, I did not have the heart to rebuff her by saying what was on my mind. So, I smiled.

'Smiling is good for health,' the young girl filled the silence promptly. 'When you smile the world smiles with you. But when you weep you have to weep alone. Isn't that true?'

'It's a good quotation,' I said, now resigned to my fate.

'But it's not my statement. This is one of Amitabh Bachchan's dialogues. Do you like Amitabh?'

I thought I would surprise her. 'No, I like Hrithik Roshan.'

'Yes, he is extremely handsome,' she agreed, switching her loyalty from Amitabh to Hrithik in a matter of seconds.

'Hrithik looks handsome because there is a shade of shyness on his face. When there is no shyness on a young boy or girl's face, they look rather bland. Don't you think Akshaye also has a similar shyness?'

'Which Akshay?' All this time, I was answering her questions. Now, I found myself asking a question. I was getting drawn into a conversation without even realizing it. Conversation is like a whirlpool. You can get sucked into it unwittingly.

'Don't you know Akshaye? I mean, Akshaye Khanna, not Akshay Kumar. Akshaye Khanna is the son of Vinod Khanna by his first marriage. He has acted in *Taal* opposite Aishwarya Rai. Akshay Kumar is the one who recently got married to actress Twinkle Khanna.'

Her knowledge of the film industry was extensive.

A slight headache, which I had had since that morning, began to recur now. Was it the incessant talking? If one question from me could bring forth so much by way of an answer, then by the time we reached Hubli, I would be too exhausted to do any work. For a full hour and a half, she had been asking questions or talking nonstop. My headache bore witness to it.

Enough was enough, I thought. I decided to be frank with her and tell her that I wanted to catch up on my sleep. My head was throbbing by now and my hands went instinctively to my forehead to massage it.

'Are you not feeling well?' she asked with concern when she noticed this.

'Well, I had a headache in the morning,' I said. I didn't tell her that it had increased due to her incessant questions.

'Do you have any medicine with you?' she enquired.
'No.'

She opened her handbag and gave me a bottle of balm.
'This is a new product—Neeranjana Balm. It is extremely
good for headaches. You will feel fresh and nice after
using it. It is scented and also removes all body aches. It
is a non-greasy ayurvedic preparation. Less expensive than
branded balms but more effective. If you buy it in bulk
there is a discount. This is a sample piece.'

Now it was my turn to be curious. 'Where are you
working?' I asked.

'I am a salesgirl for Neeranjana Balm,' she smiled.

Yes, smiling is indeed good for one's health.

15

STOVE BURSTS OR DOWRY DEATHS?

We have a saying in Sanskrit: *Ethra naryasthu pujyanthe, ramanthethathra devatha* (God exists where women are respected). In real life, this is not true. Very few women in our country have economic independence or the freedom of choosing their husbands. Most of our women are oppressed. One of the reasons for their misery is the lack of education, which in turn leads to a lack of economic freedom. If a woman is not economically independent, then her life is quite difficult.

Once a doctor friend of mine was discussing the problem of female infanticide. Being a gynaecologist at a government hospital, she had first-hand information on this terrible subject. She asked me, 'Do you want to see the greatest misery a woman can face? Come. Let's go now and I will show you.'

She took me to the burns ward in the hospital. To negatively paraphrase the saying: 'If there is hell on earth, it is this.' The whole atmosphere was deeply depressing. Almost all the patients were female. The majority of them were in the age group of eighteen to twenty-eight years and from fairly poor backgrounds. They were all in agony, suffering from severe burns. All had the same story to tell—I wanted to cook; I lit the stove; the stove burst; the pallu of my nylon sari caught fire; this is my mistake; my husband is very good; the in-laws are like my parents.

In our country, many young married women die every day because of alleged 'stove bursts'. Why is it that nobody sues the stove manufacturer? We all know the answer. These are not stove accidents, but dowry killings. Isn't it sad that in a society where Durga is worshipped and women are called Shakthi, our sisters are burned like brinjals without any mercy? It makes me cry.

In the middle of that hellish ward was a woman who was pregnant. She was in bed number 24 and was supposed to be a 'stove burst' victim. My doctor friend told me that she might not survive. She asked me whether I wished to talk to her. I did not have the courage to face that poor girl writhing in agony. It was a difficult sight to witness. Something urged me to talk, but I did not know what to say. She sensed that I wanted to talk to her. In the middle of her pain, she took the initiative.

'Amma,' she said, 'I do not know how long I will live. But I want to tell you something. If only my parents had educated me, if I had a job, if my parents had fewer children, I would not have come to this position.' She couldn't speak any more. She screamed and flinched as the pain tormented her. Unable to witness her suffering, I came out and sat on the steps of the staircase. I was blank.

After a few minutes, I noticed an old woman crying silently in the corner. She looked tired, harassed and poor. She was all alone. I went to her and asked her what the matter was.

'I am the unfortunate mother of the patient you were

just talking to. I am praying to God that she should not survive.'

Was that mother's pain any less than her daughter's when she begged God to let her daughter die? Silent tears gave way to unabashed weeping. In the hope of calming her, I asked, 'How did the stove burst?'

'There is no stove in their house,' the woman said. 'It is all lies. We have five daughters. She is the eldest. When she was in the ninth class, we stopped her education. She was a good student, but we had no choice. I wanted someone to help me in the kitchen and look after the younger children. So, she had to leave school to take care of her little sisters though she herself was a child. After a couple of years we thought of her marriage. In our neighbourhood, girls get married early. If we do not perform the marriage early enough, what will people say? We gave her a proper dowry and a grand marriage to the best of our ability.'

How typical it all sounded! And, how predictable was what followed!

The hapless mother went on, 'They were not happy. Her husband and mother-in-law would beat her for more money. Then she would come back. We used to tell her to go back to her husband's house even though we knew that they were ill-treating her. We have unmarried daughters. If this daughter came back, what would their future be? Moreover, a girl's place after marriage is in her husband's house, isn't it?'

Who would disagree with that time-honoured principle? I asked her, 'What is your husband's job?'

She said he was a carpenter. 'He believes that we must have a male child. Only a son can make our lives better, he says.' Another light on the notions that govern the lives of many in our country.

Her sorrow seemed to abate a little, but I could see anger in her eyes. Her story continued along predictable lines. 'We thought that when she had children, things would become better. But that didn't happen. When she became pregnant, her mother-in-law came to know that it was a baby girl. Then they decided to kill my daughter. My daughter gave a dying declaration. It said that her sister-in-law had tied her hands in the middle of the night, that her useless husband had poured kerosene over her and that her mother-in-law had lit the match. My doll-like daughter burnt like camphor in no time.'

Inconsolable grief burst forth from that helpless mother, tears flowing like a river. I didn't know what to say. I just mumbled, 'Do not worry. The law will take its course and they will be punished.'

But it turned out that that possibility also had been taken care of. The husband had threatened that if she told the truth, he would harm her sisters and ruin all their hopes of marriage. So she had taken back her dying declaration. Thus the culprits were safe and one more girl was sacrificed on the altar of society's greed. I could now understand the poor girl's words. If she had been educated, she could have taken up a job and left her husband. If her parents had fewer children, then they could have kept and cared for her. Her parents were more worried about how people talked about them than the fate that awaited their daughter.

The case of this pregnant girl would end like any other 'stove burst' story. Her husband would go free. He would marry again. And similar incidents would be repeated. The problem continues because there is no immediate punishment of the offenders. Even when cases are registered, they drag on in courts for years. The greed for material things is growing, so people go for easy dowry money.

Ethra naryasthu pujyanthe, ramanthe . . . Those words came back to me. Without my knowing it, tears welled up in my eyes.

The duty sister came and announced expressionlessly, 'Patient in bed number 24 is dead.'

16

IDEALISTS AT TWENTY, REALISTS AT FORTY

Recently we had a get-together of old friends. We are a group of women who have known each other since the time we were little girls. We began meeting before we were married. We kept up the practice after our marriages and after becoming mothers, and now we meet at our children's weddings. Age, of course, shows its marks on us, but we go on meeting once in a while to exchange notes. Sometimes one of us joins the get-together after a gap of several years, but we quickly take up the thread and connect.

So much has changed in the last twenty-five years. Many of these changes would have been very difficult to imagine before they happened. We had many dreams and very few of them have been realized. My friend Vimla, for example, was a very beautiful girl when we were in college. Everyone used to mistake her for a film star. She was aware of her beauty and quite vain. When we met after twenty-five years, I could not believe that the woman in front of me was Vimla. Where had her long, jet-black hair gone? Where was that perfect complexion? She looked like a barrel with wrinkles all over. Her hair was grey, thin, and cut short. She talked philosophically. Beauty is impermanent. When you are young, you think your beauty will last forever. But beauty is not like intelligence, she said. Intelligent people remain intelligent forever.

My friend Vinutha proved this theory of Vimla's wrong. Vinutha was a very bright girl in our college. She was easily one of the best students. She used to be called a mini-computer. She was gifted in every aspect—she was good-looking, talented and, more importantly, very simple. There were no airs about her. We all used to wonder whom Vinutha would marry. She was so good that it would be difficult to find an equally good match. Vinutha did find a good boy while she was in college. He was very bright. We all felt that Vinutha and Partha would always remain happy and proud of each other's intelligence. How wrong we were!

When I met Vinutha after many years, she looked dull. She had lost her zest for life. When she was in college, she was so full of energy. Be it a college day or cooking competition or math quiz, she would be more involved than anyone else. But now her spirit was dampened by her ever-taunting husband.

'Did you get a rank?' he would needle her. Often he would ask, 'Can you not understand such a simple thing?' Or he would challenge, 'Let us see how much time you take to solve this problem and how much time I take?'

Vinutha began to feel that it was a curse to be so bright. Our society is strange. The woman always enjoys her husband's glory and fame, but the reverse is seldom true. Rarely do men appreciate their wives' talents.

Ratna, on the other hand, was a very ordinary girl in

every sense of the word. The unremarkable sort of person whom people seldom remember. She graduated, married and settled down like most of our middle-class or lower-middle-class people do. Ratna's husband, Raghu, was a clerk and a very timid person.

One year, when Ratna came for our get-together, we were all astounded. She had become so different. She was a leading businesswoman now and had received many awards. She was very fashionable too. So remarkable was the transformation that we just stared at her for a while. Vimla asked Ratna to tell us her story.

'It's the typical rags-to-riches story all right,' said Ratna. 'After marriage, I realized that my husband was an excellent assistant rather than a leader. He always listened to somebody. In the family, my mother-in-law was the boss.'

Psychiatrists say that if parents are very domineering then the child will either become very rebellious and difficult to control or else become timid and docile. Maybe Ratna's Raghu belonged to the latter category.

Ratna continued: 'I realized that I had to make my own decisions, otherwise I would remain forever a slave to my mother-in-law. I decided that I must become economically independent. I was not very talented or skilled, as you know. My academic record was average. With this background, it was difficult to get a job. The one thing I knew was stitching garments. So, I started stitching at home. Initially, I worked with cloth and later with leather. I soon understood the business very well and expanded my work to suit the tastes of my customers.'

'When did you shift to condiments?' we asked.

'Once I was successful with garments, I diversified to home products. Nothing succeeds like success. I always consider the customer as a god. Work for the customer's satisfaction, not for your satisfaction—that principle pays. Life is a great teacher. I learnt everything by experience. By learning something from each of my mistakes, I learnt not to repeat them.'

We were both surprised and delighted at Ratna's courage and the turnaround in her life. We had all thought that Vinutha would be very successful and Ratna would be mediocre. But things turned out totally different. At twenty we were idealists, at forty we had become realists.

17

WHAT IS A RED-LETTER DAY? A HOLIDAY

The fifteenth of August is a red-letter day for all of us. That day in 1947 we earned our freedom from long foreign rule, after many people had sacrificed their lives for it. Even children, women and old people had participated in that struggle at great cost to themselves. However, most of them are not remembered today. Their statues are not erected and no poems are written about their sacrifices. They are unsung heroes. They died so that we could live in a free India.

To mark this as a memorable day, our government has declared Independence Day as an important national holiday. On 15 August, we are to remember our martyrs and celebrate our freedom. Normally, lectures and seminars about our independence struggle are arranged in schools and government offices. There are flag hoisting ceremonies at which patriotic songs are sung. Children enjoy and remember this special day.

One Independence Day, I was on one of my week-long tours in a rural area in Karnataka. That year, 15 August fell on a Friday. I thought I would visit some schools and participate in their celebrations. As I was staying in a town, I had to go to the bus stand to travel to a village school seven kilometres away.

At the bus stand, I met the headmaster of one of the schools I wanted to visit. He was very happy to see me and greeted me warmly. He had one of those faces that reflect feelings—a rather rare phenomenon. There are people whose feelings you cannot gauge by looking at their faces. In such cases, it seems like there is no connection between their hearts and their brains. You cannot make out what such people are thinking. This is common in big cities. In smaller places, people are usually more open.

The headmaster seemed to be in a hurry. 'Madam, are you going to Bangalore?' he asked eagerly. Then he followed up his question with an explanation. 'If you are not working on Saturday, this is going to be a long weekend. So, I thought that instead of staying here, you may be going back to Bangalore.'

'No, I am not going to Bangalore,' I said. 'I have a week's work in this area. It is a waste of time to go and come back.'

There was a trace of disappointment on his face and I was curious to know the reason. He explained, 'Oh, I thought I could travel with you. I am leaving for Bangalore.'

Suddenly, I remembered that it was 15 August.

'Wait a minute,' I said, 'today is 15 August. Aren't you celebrating Independence Day in your school? This must be a great event for teachers and students, with flag hoisting, parades and patriotic songs.'

He did not look enthusiastic at all. 'No. This is a ritual every year and a sheer waste of time. The same drill and the same patriotic songs. In my twenty years of service and ten transfers, I have grown bored with these national holidays. We cannot close the school either. As per instructions from the higher education department, we have to conduct all these activities. I wish they would make it a complete holiday like Diwali or Christmas.'

I realized that he was unhappy. So I asked him, 'Why are you going to Bangalore?'

'I want to go and stay there for two days and find out who is concerned with my transfer to the district headquarters. My daughter wants to study computer science. Don't you think it is a good idea to study computer science and get a job? If a girl is a graduate in computer science, then getting a groom will be easy.'

Perhaps he was more of a father than a headmaster. What he was talking about did not really register with me because I was still thinking about Independence Day. 'Who will conduct today's functions in your school?' I asked.

He looked at me with pity. 'What is there in a function? I have told my assistant master to conduct this ritual. I prepared speeches for this day twenty years ago. Nothing has changed. So he can read the same speech. I have not even gone to the school. The students are not interested in the speeches or in these celebrations. There is a new film in the tent near our village. They would like to go there. Nobody is bothered about Independence Day.'

I was immersed in my thoughts. Then the bus came. There was a rush and the headmaster ran to get a seat. He waved to me and got in. The bus left in a cloud of dust.

I returned to Bangalore the following week. I went to a friend's house for dinner. She is also a teacher, so we have many things in common. Both of us are so immersed in work that we hardly meet, even though we live in the same city. We have found that the best way to meet once in a while is to have dinner together.

I asked her, 'How did you and your school celebrate 15 August?'

She looked sad. 'It was horrible. We teachers went to the school early in the morning for the flag hoisting. We had invited a senior government official to be the chief guest. Poor chap! He had prepared a long speech and come on time. But . . .' she stopped.

The memory of my meeting with the headmaster of the village school a week earlier was still fresh in my mind. 'Was there any problem with the headmistress? Did she come?' I asked.

'Yes, our headmistress is a nice person. She was on time although she was suffering from high fever. It was our students who didn't come. Though our school has more than a thousand students, only about fifty of them turned up that day.'

'Why?'

'It happened to be a long weekend. Parents took their children away on holiday. Many students who stayed in Bangalore were seen at the theatres. Apparently, there was heavy rush at video shops as well that day. It was a bad show in front of our chief guest.'

'Wasn't attendance mandatory?'

'Yes, we sent notices stating that children must be

brought to school that day. But what is the use? They will just produce false medical certificates. At times, I feel we should just not have a holiday on 15 August or 26 January. We should have regular school and one or two periods can be used for the function. Today, it has become a holiday only to make merry, not a day to remember the saga of our leaders. What do you think?'

I didn't know what to say.

18

Once Upon A Time, Life was Simple

I was born and brought up in a village in northern Karnataka. Things were very simple in those days. If you didn't like a person, you could just tell him to his face why you were upset with him. If somebody helped you, you could show your gratitude without any reservation. If somebody did wrong, we asked for justice. There was no hide-and-seek when it came to feelings. Maybe it was not civilized or polished behaviour, but it was definitely a straightforward society and a simple life.

I do not know how societies in villages function today. In my childhood, village societies functioned smoothly and fairly. I still remember vividly the day our cow was lost. We came to know that it was tied up in Gopal's cowshed. Immediately, he was called by the elders of the panchayat. Gopal owned a piece of land where he used to grow vegetables. Selling them on market day was his only source of income. Our cow had run away and gone into Gopal's garden where it had eaten up all the fresh vegetables. Naturally, Gopal was very upset and had tied up the cow. We felt genuinely sorry and offered to compensate Gopal's loss. He agreed immediately and released the cow. No legal code was referred to and no lawyer was called. The panchayat made the decision, calculated the loss and solved the problem amicably. There were no ill feelings between the parties concerned.

I remember another incident. In our neighbour's family, a girl was having problems with her mother-in-law. Mothers-in-law harassing daughters-in-law is an age-old problem in all communities, irrespective of language or culture. An old Chinese proverb says: 'Is it ever possible for a mouse and a cat to be friends?' There are, of course, exceptions, but these only prove the general rule.

The young daughter-in-law from our neighbour's house used to come to the village pond to fetch water. She was hardly twenty years old, delicate and sensitive. At the pond, she would usually be alone and she would sit on the steps and cry. Evidently, she was going through a rough time at home.

My old grandmother saw the girl crying. She understood the problem. Immediately, she went to the neighbour's house, called the mother-in-law outside and told her, 'Don't be harsh to your daughter-in-law. Please remember that your daughter is also a daughter-in-law in another house. I have seen you as a young bride. There is always a court above and you have to answer for all your deeds.'

My grandmother never felt that it was none of her business to get involved in somebody else's family matter. For her, injustice to a lonely young girl was more than a 'personal matter'. After some time, our neighbour mended her ways. More importantly, she never held a grudge against my grandmother. She knew, as people of that generation always did, that it was important to listen to one's elders. A sense of fairness and respect for elders were fundamental values in those times. Common sense reigned. Rules and legalities were secondary to plain and simple common sense.

My father passed away recently. There was a cooking gas connection in his name. I thought it would be illegal to keep the connection after his death, so I submitted an application for transferring the connection to my name, along with his death certificate and my ration card. One day, I was called to the gas agency.

'Your application is incomplete,' the manager told me. 'Though your father has left a will stating that you should inherit his gas connection, there is no legal document on paper in which your brothers and sisters tell us that they will not claim this gas. In the absence of that document, it is illegal to transfer the connection to your name.'

I told him that my sister and brother were American citizens living abroad, and that they were not interested in this gas connection. But he was an official with an official mind. Common sense was of no value to him. Rules alone mattered.

He said, 'You should get a notary certificate from America regarding this connection.'

I was taken aback by the sudden complication in what I had thought would be a simple procedure in light of my father's will.

When I mentioned this, the manager turned even more uncooperative. 'Madam, nobody is above the law. So what if they are American citizens? They must follow the rules. I don't want to get into any problems for this later.'

It is difficult to get notary authorization in America for such a small thing. You have to take half a day's leave for this kind of work. Of course, the manager didn't accept any of my arguments. I left the gas office dejected. After a month, when I wanted to refill the gas, the manager stuck to his rule book. 'Your father is no more. You cannot take a cylinder in his name.'

It struck me that if I had not informed him about my father's death, things would have been simpler. Many of us try to do what is lawful and proper, only to realize that our system is not made for such behaviour.

There is a woman working as a sweeper on my road whom I have known for a long time. The other day I saw her crying. I felt bad for her. The reason for her unhappiness was her husband, who often got drunk and beat her. I could not resist the urge to go and advise her husband. Perhaps the influence of my grandmother was working on me. My neighbours saw her crying too but did not bother about it or care to talk to her husband. Maybe they were wiser. For when I talked to her husband, he turned around and said, 'Madam, it is none of your business to interfere in our personal life. This is a matter between a husband and wife. If I cause any problems, then my wife can go to a lawyer. She need not come to you.'

I did not know how to respond. When he talked about law, I wondered what law meant to us. Laws are made to create a strong society that will protect the common people. But when laws become difficult to follow, their very purpose is lost. When they are interpreted narrowly by over-zealous officials, their purpose is lost too.

What can ordinary people do about this? We have to deal with a range of ordinary problems, from gas connections to drunken husbands. Can some learned lawyers suggest solutions to these day-to-day problems?

19

Powerful Politicians and Unsung Donors

Honours are quite often bestowed upon people in power. Whether they deserve the honour or not is immaterial. What matters is the power they wield. Those who bestow the honour have some expectations from those honoured. Sometimes, I feel that there should be no honours at all because beneath every shawl and garland there is an application.

The Infosys Foundation built an annexe to an existing government hospital in one of the states where we work. The hospital was in a small town and our Foundation had no interest there other than helping the poor. It was a very backward area. The inaugural function was held on the hospital premises. The chief guest was the health minister of the state. I had requested the function coordinator to arrange it in the morning because if things got delayed, I would still be able to drive back safely. I do not like the idea of travelling alone by road at night. But the coordinator could not oblige. A morning function was not convenient for the chief guest, so the inauguration was fixed for seven in the evening.

The dais was arranged with quite a number of chairs. There were a dozen or more garlands of jasmine, sandalwood and marigold, varieties of shawls and baskets full of colourful fruit kept on the dais for distribution. There was also a silk sari in a box, probably an expensive one. They clearly had spent a great deal of money on all these things.

In the kind of welfare work I am engaged in, we don't expect much from the beneficiaries. When they say a few good words about our work, we feel a sense of satisfaction. Often these words are the inspiration for our next job. It also means that the beneficiaries appreciate our donation. I sat there thinking about how grateful the people were, how they were honouring us because we built a hospital for them and how graceful their culture was.

The breeze was cool and the crowd kept getting bigger. The minister arrived an hour late and the people rushed to touch his feet. Some people came running with applications. Soon it was like a mini-durbar.

The function finally started. I was given a corner seat on the dais. There were plenty of speeches describing how efficient the minister was, how great his leadership was and how fond he was of his fellow men. Under his able leadership, a new hospital building had been added by a donor. In all those speeches, there was not a single mention of the donor's identity or even the hospital. It was all about the minister and the government.

The minister then rose to inaugurate the building. He said he had great faith in democracy and that he cared for his people immensely. He wanted this annexe to the hospital because he was concerned about the people's health. He said that he was still not happy because the hospital required more facilities. Then he turned to look at me and said, 'Madam, we expect fans, beds, cupboards, linen, drinking water facility and so on for the entire hospital. I am sure you people will be able to provide these. I assure you that our people will make the best use of these.'

I did not answer.

Then came the most important part of the ceremony, that of honouring the people who had helped to build the hospital. It was followed by the national anthem. Then the function was over. The minister rushed back to his car and everyone ran behind him. Soon the whole area was deserted. Crushed flowers were strewn around the dais. Except for the pandal area, it was pitch-dark outside. I stood there with a faded garland and my handbag. I was all alone, like a goalpost after the match.

In front of me was the illuminated new building erected by our Foundation. I was by no means the only one who had put in hard work. There were architects, artisans, trustees and several others. None of their names had been mentioned. There was no time for them or for our Foundation. I was clearly an unwanted guest and had been called only for formality's sake.

I was feeling quite depressed about the whole evening. I wondered why they did not even have the simple courtesy of caring for a lady, especially one who had come from far away and represented a charitable organization. Look at these people, I said to myself. This health minister had in no way contributed time, money or resources for building this annexe. He was not even aware that it was being built. But he saw to it that he was honoured and praised like a hero. He was garlanded the most. Was it just politics or was it moral corruption?

I reminded myself that the ultimate aim of our work was not to please ministers, politicians, rich people or people in power. Every effort of ours was aimed at improving the lot of suffering people. Not the minister, but the poor people were the ones who mattered.

My depression did not last long. An old lady in tattered clothes came up to me and said, 'Amma, someone told me that your company has built this building. We are very grateful to you. Many people like us never get admission in the main hospital because of lack of space. But you have given us a common space, with no special wards. Special rooms will always be used by people with connections. For people like us, common halls are better.'

Then she took a step closer to me and said, 'I don't have anything to give you. I am just a flower vendor. I cannot afford a shawl or a sari. But I can give you this string of jasmine flowers with love and affection. I pray to God that many people like you should be born in our country.'

That string of jasmine was more precious than all the shawls and fruit baskets.

Leprosy. Just the word scares most people. There is an international convention that discourages the use of the word 'leper' because of its terrible connotations. The moment we think of a person afflicted with leprosy we think of a beggar or a person who has lost some fingers or toes. People suffering from leprosy are often ostracized by society. There are many myths regarding this dreaded disease—that it is contagious, that it is hereditary, and so on. These are just myths. In fact, not all cases of leprosy are contagious. If proper treatment is taken at an early stage, leprosy can be cured completely, leaving behind none of the telltale physical disfigurement that sometimes accompanies the disease. Normally, the treatment period is long. It requires a lot of patience and family support. Due to ignorance, however, people neglect early symptoms. Detection in the initial stages often does not take place, though the media carries advertisements about how to recognize the symptoms. Most people just don't bother. We always think that leprosy is a problem that affects other people, not us. We forget that disease knows no social hierarchy; it does not distinguish between rich or poor, man or woman. And leprosy is a disease that has been with mankind for many centuries.

One of the programmes of the organization with which I am associated is to help people suffering from leprosy. There are different theories in this field. Some people think that the patients should stay with their families, while others believe they should be kept in an isolated colony. I was working in a remote area where there was a separate colony for leprosy patients. It was a hot summer and temperatures were difficult to bear. The scene at the colony was depressing. Most of the inmates were clearly disgusted with the disease and their sufferings. They were all poor and helpless. They required psychological as well as material help. Even soothing words like, 'Don't worry, we're here with you,' were important to them.

Our project's aim was not to show pity or to hand out money. We planned to rehabilitate the patients economically. If they could handle even some limited work and earn their own livelihood, then we were ready to finance them. We figured it was the best way to make them feel confident. For when a person feels confident, he can face society. Acceptance by society and a reasonable measure of economic independence can change the lives of these people.

There were many huts in the colony, with a family staying in each hut. In every family, at least one person was afflicted by the disease. The weather was harsh but I had to do my duty and go from hut to hut. The women kept telling me their difficulties. Perhaps the most frustrating of these was their inability to get jobs even as housemaids because of the disease. Some of them had resigned themselves to their fate. Youngsters were sleeping even though it was only mid-morning. Children were playing in the dirt. The older people were in a pathetic state. When the infirmities of age are added to the ravages of a disease like leprosy and the consequent social ostracism, people can be driven to suicide.

There was a small hut with a thatched roof, clay walls and the bare semblance of a bamboo door. A woman lived there, the oldest in the colony. Her name was Veeramma. I called out to her and asked her to come out. She did not. I thought she might be partially deaf and that it would be better if I went in to talk to her. I knocked carefully at what passed for a door, lest it fall down. She still did not respond or come out. I pushed the door open and went in.

There was hardly anything in the hut. Holes in the roof let in some air and light. There were two or three earthen pots and one earthen plate. Three stones made up a stove. There was a torn mat, two or three onions on the ground and a pot of water. I still could not see Veeramma inside the hut, but I could hear the sound of breathing. As I had entered the hut from the bright sunlight outside, it took my eyes a while to adjust to the darkness inside.

I called out to her softly once more, 'Veeramma, I want to talk to you. Where are you?'

Then she answered, 'Amma, I am here. But don't come near me.'

Now I could see the frail form of a woman in the corner of the room, all her hairy grey skin shrunk, no flesh on the body. She was just a skeleton covered with skin. She was sitting in a corner holding her hands against her chest, her legs also drawn towards her chest.

'Amma,' she mumbled, 'I know you called me several times, but I could not come out to talk to you. I am a woman. Irrespective of my age, how can I come out in front of other people without any clothes?'

It was then that I realized that she was almost naked.

I have seen poverty-stricken areas in the course of my work and I have met a lot of poor people, but nowhere had I seen a woman like this. This was a picture of dehumanizing poverty in our own country after fifty years of independence. An old woman could not even cover her body. Still she had no complaints about anything. I felt guilty wearing a six-yard sari.

For a minute, I felt too ashamed to talk. The shock of what I saw made me forget our policy of simply not handing out money and material. This was a situation that cried out for immediate remedy. I sent my driver to get 100 saris to be given to all the women in that colony. Whether they are rehabilitated or not, the minimum need of covering a woman's body could not wait. A gesture like this may not change a great deal in their lives. But the sight of abject misery often prods us into action, even if it is just an impulse. Those of us who have a generous share of God's blessings must do what we can to help the poorest of the poor who are wretched through no fault of theirs.

India does not always mean technology, fashion, films or beauty contests. The real India is in the dark, neglected interiors of our country. Helpless and miserably poor people live beyond the reach of any government departments. To serve our country means to serve such people.

After that visit to the colony of leprosy patients, I make it a point to carry at least ten saris with me whenever I go on my rounds.

SALAAM NAMASTE

I used to buy books for the Bangalore slum schools we supported from Sheikh Mohammed's tiny shop. He had a shop selling stationery near our office and we would buy the books in bulk from him. We would pick up the books from the shop and let him know when the cheque was ready. He would then come to the office and collect it.

Once, when he came to the office to get his cheque, we were celebrating something and sweets were being handed out to everyone. Sheikh was offered some as well. He took a couple and put them away carefully in his pocket. Seeing him do that, I asked, 'What's the matter, Sheikh? Why aren't you eating the sweets? Are you a diabetic?'

Sheikh was a shy, taciturn man and I knew little about him and his family, so I was pleasantly surprised to hear his explanation: 'No, madam. I'm going to take them home and give them to the kids. They love these sweets.'

'How many children do you have?' I had noticed he had picked up only a couple of pieces.

'I have one daughter, but my niece also stays with us, so there are two children in the house.'

'Why does your niece stay with you?'

'She is my sister Zubeida's daughter. She is a widow

and both stay with us.'

I realized it must be tough for Sheikh to manage a fairly large household with only the income from his little shop. So I asked, 'Does Zubeida work?'

'Yes, she is a very good tailor. She and my wife do tailoring at home. With their income and the money I earn from the shop we get by quite well. We are contented.'

I was touched by his story. 'Contented' is a word rarely heard these days. A few months passed and one day I suddenly got a call from Sheikh. He wanted me to give him his cheque a few days earlier than usual. 'Why, Sheikh? Is anything the matter?' I asked.

'Yes, madam. We discovered some time back that Zubeida is suffering from cancer. The operation is tomorrow and we need the money desperately.'

I instructed the cheque be sent to him immediately, but I also realized that it would probably not be enough. Such operations are expensive and I was sure he was struggling to raise the money. Yet he had asked me only for what was due to him and nothing more.

I have learnt many lessons in life ever since we started helping people monetarily through the Infosys Foundation. I have seen women hiding their diamond studs in their purses and asking for funds for the poor. I have seen well-off parents declaring their children orphans and applying for scholarships. I even know some men who presented their parents as destitutes so they could get help from us.

I called up Sheikh. 'Sheikh, tell me, have you managed to get all the money you need for the operation?'

'I have sold all of Zubeida's and my wife's jewellery. I

have also taken a loan from the bank.'

'Sheikh, why didn't you ask us?'

'Madam, at least I can afford this much. You should be helping those who are poorer and cannot even afford this. They require your help more than I do.'

I was touched. I asked him to get the papers and meet me as quickly as he could. He came the next morning and showed me all the documents. I took a look and handed him a cheque for fifty thousand rupees.

Surprised and hesitant, he said, 'This is a lot of money. I never expected such help to come from the blue. May you be blessed forever.'

A few days passed and Sheikh sent a message saying the operation had gone well. For a long time after that we did not hear anything from him. Then one day as I walked into the office I found him sitting in the reception, a little girl of about four by his side. She was wearing an ordinary cotton dress decorated with laces and buttons. Her hair, neatly oiled, was pulled up into a ponytail.

'How are you, Sheikh?' I asked him. 'How is Zubeida?'

Sheikh's face was lined with grief. 'Zubeida passed away a fortnight back. In spite of all our efforts and your help she did not survive. It was Allah's wish. I wanted you to meet her daughter Tabassum.'

I looked at Tabassum. She was scared and ill at ease in this strange office where people bustled about busily. Just to make her feel comfortable, I offered her some biscuits. She took one and then asked me in a shy voice, 'Can I take another one? For Ameena?'

Ameena was her cousin. I smiled and said, 'Of course.'

I looked sadly at the girl, orphaned so young. Then her uncle said, '*Beti, Ammi ne bola than na? Inko salaam karo.*' Putting down the biscuits, the little girl said in a clear voice, 'Madam, *Ammi ka salaam.*'

I was at a loss for words. Sheikh wiped his tears and pulled out an envelope from his bag. He handed it to me saying, 'This is yours. I am sorry, I am a bit late with this.'

I opened it. There were three thousand rupees in it. I looked at Sheikh in confusion. 'Out of the fifty thousand you gave us, we used only forty-seven thousand for Zubeida's treatment. When we came home and she knew she was dying, Zubeida made me promise that I would return the remaining money to you. "Don't waste this on me," she said. "Tell madam to give it to some other sick person." She had wanted so much to meet you and give you her salaam, but Allah took her away. I promised her I would carry out this last wish.'

I sat there in stunned silence. I had never met Zubeida, but the largeness of her heart even on her deathbed left me speechless. In spite of her own pain and poverty, she had thought about someone who might be in greater need of help. Her story was a lesson in compassion. She wanted to thank me, and when she knew she would not make it, she sent her daughter. Through the act of sending Tabassum she was perhaps passing on her positive attitude to the child. I was sure Tabassum would grow up to be a fine human being. I looked at the envelope. 'This is for Tabassum. May Allah be kind to her. Let her study well. If you need any more help for her, let me know. And always tell her about her mother. Our earth is enriched by people like Zubeida.'

Tabassum sat quietly, her big eyes puzzled. One day she would understand and perhaps emulate her mother's courage.

22

A Wedding to Remember

As a trustee of the Infosys Foundation, I get stacks of letters. We help people financially for various reasons. Naturally, both needy and not-so-needy people write to us. The most difficult aspect of this job is to tell the difference between both kinds of people.

One typical Monday morning, letters poured in. I was going through the letters. My secretary told me, 'Ma'am, there is a wedding invitation card with a personal note attached to it. Will you be attending?'

As a teacher in a college, I get many wedding invitations from my students, so I assumed the card was from one of my students. But when I read the card, I was unable to remember either of the persons getting married. I wondered who could have sent me an invitation with a hand-written note stating, 'Madam, if you do not attend our marriage, we will consider it unfortunate.'

I was still not able to place the girl's or the boy's name, but I decided to attend the wedding out of curiosity. It was the rainy season and the venue was at the other end of the city. I wondered if attending some unknown person's wedding was worth the trouble.

It was a typical middle-class wedding with a stage decorated profusely with flowers. Film music, which nobody was listening to, was blaring over the speakers. Because of the rain, the numerous children in attendance were not able to play outside and were playing hide-and-seek in the hall. Women were wearing Bangalore silk saris and Mysore crepes.

I looked at the couple standing on the dais. I still was unable to remember either of them. I thought that perhaps one or both of them might have been my students. Standing in the middle of the crowd, without knowing anybody, I didn't know what to do.

Just then, an elderly man approached me and asked politely, 'Would you like to meet the couple and greet them?'

I followed him to the dais, introduced myself and wished the couple a happy married life. They seemed very happy. The groom asked the elderly man to look after me. Still the question nagged me: who were these people and why had they sent a note to me?

The man took me to the dining hall and brought me something to eat. Enough is enough, I thought to myself. I can't eat without knowing who these people are.

Sensing my doubts, the elderly gentleman smiled and said, 'Madam, I am the groom's father. My son fell in love with Malati, the bride, and we arranged the wedding. After the engagement, Malati developed leucoderma. My son backed out of the marriage. We all felt very sad. I asked him what he would have done if Malati had got leucoderma after marriage, but he would not listen. Her family was worried about her future. There was so much unpleasantness. To escape from the tension at home, my son began to go to the library often. After about a month, he came back and told me that he was ready to marry Malati. We were all pleasantly surprised and were truly happy. Today is the marriage.'

I still did not have an answer to my question. How on earth was I involved in this? The groom's father provided the answer.

'Madam, later we came to know that he read your novel, *Mahashweta*,' he said. 'The situation of my son was similar. It seems he read this novel at least ten times and understood the plight of the girl. He took a month and decided he did not want to be like the man in your novel, who shed his responsibilities only to regret it later. Your novel changed his thinking.'

Now I could put the pieces together! Then the groom's father brought a packet and insisted that I accept the gift. When I hesitated, he pressed it into my hands and said, 'Malati has purchased this sari for you. She will talk to you later.'

The rain grew heavier and water splashed into the hall. Raindrops were falling on my face; my silk sari was getting wet. But nothing mattered. I felt so happy. Never in my wildest dreams had I thought that an ordinary person like myself would change somebody's life. Whenever I wear that sari, I think of the happy face of Malati and the cover page of *Mahashweta*. It's the most precious sari I own.

February is usually a season of house-warming functions, thread ceremonies and quick weddings, particularly for software engineers who come back from the USA on short visits. It is also the time for students to prepare for their examinations.

My friend Suma had purchased a house and was keen that her close friends attend the house-warming ceremony. For us, it was an occasion to get together after a long time. The traditional ceremony was going on when I reached her house at an early hour. The other friends had not yet come. I found a place to sit and watch the puja while waiting for my friends. Though the house was quite a big one, the puja was being performed in a small hall and just two carpets had been spread for the guests to sit on. Suma was busy doing the puja. She was wearing a beautiful silk sari and the flowers in her hair added to her grace. As usual, the majority of the guests had nothing to do and were thus engrossed in chatting about a variety of topics—the problems of teenagers, the Prime Minister, gossip about Madhuri Dixit, Miss India, the best beauty parlours, the latest fashion jewellery . . . the list was endless. However, it was the subject of in-laws that received the maximum attention and active participation from many.

Though I was listening to the conversation, there was an altogether different thought at the back of my mind. It had been hardly a week since the Gujarat earthquake and almost all the TV channels had been telecasting the latest information. Although I did not know the victims personally, just the thought of their plight sent a shiver through my body and tears welled up in my eyes. All this was on my mind constantly.

Though I was not taking part in the conversation, I could not help but hear what some of the guests were saying.

'Look at Suma, lucky person. She got such a beautiful house at a good price.' There was a tinge of envy in the woman's tone.

'How much did she pay?'

'Hardly fifty lakhs. It was a distress sale. I know the man who owned the house.'

'Why was there a distress sale?'

'He owned a factory and the recession hit his business badly. So he had to close the factory and sell the house.'

'This house is so beautiful—all marble flooring and attached bathrooms with fitted tubs. It's a steal for this price.'

'By the way, how are the preparations for your daughter's wedding getting along?'

'I thought it is better to go to Kanchipuram and buy all the saris there. It works out cheaper and the choice of colour combinations is better.'

'What about silverware?'

'That is no problem. I know a person in Chickpet. He

is our silversmith. I've told him to make one hundred silver *kumkum bharanis* and one hundred small silver bowls. The *bharanis* will be given to distant relatives and the bowls to the closer people.'

'Have you thought of the catering?'

'Am I a fool not to think about catering? I have discussed with my children and husband in detail. We have decided to have pani puri, bhel and chat stalls on one side and south Indian snacks on the other side. Cool drinks and sweets are also included. We all love Gujarati sweets, but our cook has gone to Gujarat. He has lost his family. I wouldn't want him to come to the wedding because it is inauspicious.'

'By the way, how much did you contribute to the earthquake relief fund?'

'They were collecting money in my office. But I told them that I had given money elsewhere and did not participate. Our country is always facing one problem or another. There is no end to the problems. So why pay? Anyway, I don't have any relatives in that area.'

I wondered what our so-called upper-middle-class people were doing for Gujarat. Is it not a part of our country? I do agree that life is larger than death. One cannot go on mourning forever. But is our life full of only silver *kumkum bharanis*, Kanchipuram saris and wedding menus? Our children learn from watching us. If we all behave in this way, our next generation will also have the same insensitive minds.

I remembered the story of a young prince with a beautiful wife and child. When he saw a sick person, an old person and a dead body, he renounced the world, became an ascetic and preached in our land. What would his social sensitivity index have been? How much have we learnt from him?

Asha and I were shopping on MG Road when we saw an old man walking slowly towards us. He might have been around sixty, with silver-grey hair and a few wrinkles on his face, but he still looked fit. He looked at Asha and smiled. She did not show any sign of recognition. The man stood in front of us for a second and then walked away.

After he left, I asked her, 'Asha, don't you think that man knows you? He smiled at you. Do you remember him?'

'Of course I know him. He was my maths teacher in school. He taught us very badly and ruined my interest in maths. He was a terror, unapproachable and stern. He hardly taught us.' There was anger and frustration in Asha's voice. She might have exaggerated.

It is true that school teachers, more than college teachers, build your fundamentals. It is easy to teach at graduate and postgraduate levels, but difficult to do so at the school level. Teachers—good ones at least—must have an enormous amount of love for their students. Knowledge is not the only criterion to judge a teacher.

I thought of my own maths teacher. I wondered how I would have reacted had he met me on the road. What would he have done and how would he have greeted me? He probably would have said, 'Why are you wasting your time on MG Road? Go back to office or work at home. Don't teach without preparation.'

Without a second thought, I would have said, 'Yes sir.' Then, hesitantly, I would have asked, 'Where are you staying? Can I come and see you some time later?'

He would have patted me on my shoulder with the same affection and concern that he showed me as a student and both of us would have laughed.

My teacher, Raghavendra Varnekar, was an extraordinary man in every sense of the word. He was from my home town, Hubli. He lived a very humble life and did not receive any recognition or awards. He excelled in his profession even though he was not a graduate. He taught mathematics so well that we never felt it was a difficult subject.

He would refer to mathematics as the 'queen of science'. 'Let us go and meet the queen,' he would say as he led us into the wonderland of mathematics. There were numerous riders in geometry, hundreds of problems in algebra. He would teach them enthusiastically and say, 'I am here for students who believe they are not good in maths. Good and bad are concepts of the mind. If you are hard-working and honestly want to understand the subject, then you can have an audience with the queen.' He attracted students to his class the way a snake charmer attracts snakes with his music.

In his last days, he was unwell and I went to meet him with a small gift. In spite of his financial difficulties, he did not accept it. He told me, 'The duty of a teacher is to make a student confident to face life. Life poses unknown examinations. The greatest joy to a teacher is to produce students better than him. I have done my duty very well. My students are so famous today that it gives me great joy and pride to be recognized as their teacher.'

I was surprised to hear this simple philosophy, which is very difficult to practise. Had he been in a bigger city and working in a bigger school, he would have made money by taking tuitions or by starting a school himself. He did not do that. He believed in his principle and his life was an example of it. He reminds me of a burning candle—giving light to everybody while burning itself out.

Today, when I stand on a dais and speak confidently or face any kind of difficulty in life, I think of my teacher. He taught me this lesson, which no amount of money can buy, no difficulties can dilute and no university can grant.

25

Pay or I'll Commit Suicide

At the Infosys Foundation we get approximately 10,000 letters annually. It is a Herculean task for my secretaries to sort them, read them and send replies. Some letters are eye-openers and some are funny and crazy. One day I received a letter that seemed like an SOS. It was a five-page letter from a woman. The first two pages described the vagaries of the stock market. She explained how she had lost her money by choosing the wrong stocks. The actual message was in the last few sentences. She asked me to pay all the loans she had incurred due to her foolishness. 'It is not a big amount. It is a mere five crores,' she concluded. I didn't know who this woman was and marvelled at her audacity in writing a letter like this. I didn't reply.

The very next week there was another letter from her, again five pages long, but this time describing her domestic difficulties and how important it was for me to help her. She also wrote that she would commit suicide if I did not send her the money, and that she would hold me responsible. What could I reply to such a letter? I didn't write back. After two weeks, a third letter came, saying that I had a heart of stone, that I didn't have any love and sympathy for fellow human beings. She wondered how a person like me could be involved in philanthropic work.

Such letters hurt me at times. I really cannot understand this kind of philosophy. If you fail to give money when asked, you are immediately treated with hostility. Relatives often behave in the same way. They comment, 'What is the use of relatives when you do not give money to your own people? How can you help others?'

Help is a word whose real meaning very few people understand. It is essential that we help our people and our country, but giving money to a well-to-do person should not be considered help. Giving money to buy a second house, expensive jewellery or for a holiday abroad is not help. If somebody loses money on the stock market in his greed to become rich quickly, then why should anyone feel obliged to help him?

If somebody honours me with a shawl, there is usually an application that comes with it. If a person praises me, most of the time there is a request at the end. I have decided to help only people who do not have anything, people who may perish without support. These are my people. They are my relatives. I work for them, regardless of their caste, community, gender, language or political affiliation, provided that we have funds. I don't expect anything from them, not even a bouquet of flowers. The happiness in their eyes is the real reward.

After the woman's suicide threat, I asked my secretary to discard such letters without showing them to me. As a result, I have fewer letters to read these days.

26

NOT ALL'S WRONG WITH THE NEXT GENERATION

Recently, I visited Egypt. I wanted to see the oldest pyramid in the country. It is not in Giza but in Sakkara, 24 km from Cairo. It is a five-step pyramid built for the Pharaoh Zosheyer. The architect was Imenhotep, the most intelligent and wise man at that time. While I was travelling, I was accompanied by a guide who also happened to be a well-read student of Egyptology. He was describing the writings on some of the pyramids. Pointing to some inscriptions, he translated aloud, 'The children of the next generation will be spendthrifts, will not think much and will not know much about life. We do not know what their future will be. Only the sun god Ra can save them.'

While this was being read out to me, I remembered the oft-heard complaints about the next generation in our own country—that youngsters do not respect our ideas, that they are rude, that they don't read much. It struck me that every generation has the same complaints about the next one. This has been going on from generation to generation, all over the world, for at least the last 5000 years.

Today's children have far more knowledge and far less

patience compared to our generation. I casually asked my teenage son the other day, 'Tell me the three most important revolutions or ideas of the twentieth century.'

He looked at me for a while and said, 'You behave like a teacher even at home. The most important revolutions and ideas of the century, according to me, are the principle of non-violence, the effect of violence and the impact of the communication media.'

'I will explain it to you,' he went on, noticing my surprise. 'When India was enslaved for centuries, when we did not have any power to make our decisions, a thin little man started a new kind of movement without bloodshed. No weapons, no money, but a message to the rulers: "We will not cooperate with you, come what may." He won freedom for India with this new thinking. He really deserved the Nobel Prize for peace. He was Mohandas Karamchand Gandhi, the father of our nation. His revolutionary idea influenced leaders like Martin Luther King Jr, Nelson Mandela and Aung San Suu Kyi, in gaining freedom for their people.

'The second idea was almost during the same period, but in the reverse direction. This man believed in the idea of hatred. He thought he could rule people with weapons and violence. He killed people like flies. He never understood the meaning of love and kindness. He could not bring peace by his method and became the cause for World War II. Millions of people suffered because of him and his policies. His life is the best example of war, intolerance and prejudice. He was Adolf Hitler.'

I thought that my son had a point, but I still felt that

the computer was the most important invention of the twentieth century. The young teenager did not agree.

'Today the world has shrunk because of mass media. In a matter of seconds, we come to know what is happening anywhere in the world. Television and the Internet are part of it. This has cut the cost of communication and barriers are disappearing. You can see its effect in the business world as well as in social life. That doesn't mean we're losing our old culture, but I can say we're exposed to other cultures also.'

I was surprised with my son, whom long ago I had taught how to hold a pencil. Now he was talking like an experienced adult about global subjects like peace, violence and communication. I am sure that many parents will often have the same thoughts. They might have also experienced how their little ones have become wiser than themselves. Our scriptures say, 'The one who acquires knowledge should be respected, irrespective of age, gender or class.'

My son wants to study abroad and I always wondered if this little boy of mine could manage alone. After this conversation with him, I realized that this young bird's wings have become strong and healthy. The time has come for him to fly on his own and see the world.

27

THINK POSITIVE, BE HAPPY

My mother had a cook called Girija who came from a poor family. She never spoke about her personal life. She was always cheerful and neatly dressed in a cotton sari and wore flowers in her well-combed hair. She looked smart and contented. While working in the kitchen she would hum songs and comply to our requests with a smile. I never saw her sad or grumbling. The only thing we knew about her was that her husband had abandoned her and their son. With very little formal education, the opportunities in a small town were limited, so she opted to be a cook.

Vasant, a family friend of ours, was an executive with a multinational company and he used to visit us often. He was always complaining about something or the other and after each visit of his, the whole atmosphere would become gloomy.

'My son is not studying well in his 12th class,' he complained.

I knew that his son was a very bright and hardworking boy. Why was his father complaining about him?

'I want my son to get into IIT.'

In today's competitive world, there are lakhs of children trying to get admission into one of the prestigious

Indian Institutes of Technology. If a child loses even five marks in the entrance examination because of stress, his rank comes down considerably. We can tell our children to study hard, but we should not put pressure on them to get ranks ahead of others.

The next time Vasant visited us, he was unhappy for a different reason. 'I purchased a plot about five years ago. Now that I want to sell it, the price is drastically lower,' he grumbled. 'There's a slump in the market. I invested in real estate, but it has failed.'

This was a countrywide phenomenon. The housing market was going through a recession and all those who had invested in it had lost money. He was no exception. But he made it sound as though he was the sole victim of recession and that he alone was suffering.

Several days later, Vasant paid us another visit. He looked exhausted. 'Bangalore is no longer what it was,' he complained. 'Twenty years back, the summers were so beautiful that it felt like a hill station. Today we require air-conditioners or need to get away to hill stations.'

Global warming is a worldwide phenomenon. Bangalore is no special place. But still our friend would complain.

One day, when Girija and I were alone at home, I casually asked her, 'Tell me Girija, where is your husband? Do you meet him?'

She looked at me in silence and said, 'He is here with another woman and works for your neighbour as a driver.'

I was taken aback. She saw her husband every day

and that too with another woman!

'Are you not mad at him?' I asked her.

'Initially, I used to be. But now, I think I am lucky because I have only one child to support. My son is bright and obedient. Because his father deserted us, my son is more concerned about me. If I was all alone or if I had many children or if my child was irresponsible, then I would have had serious problems. God has been kind enough to me that I don't have any such problems.'

'Are you not worried about your future?'

'Why should I worry? Can worrying solve any problem? Your mother has given us a quarter to stay. I work sincerely. All of you are happy. If I need anything, I can always ask you people. For that matter, demands are never-ending. When my son grows up, he will not be like his father, because he has seen me suffer. Amma, I have not learnt much in school, but life has taught me one thing: always look at life in a positive way. You feel nice and so do the people around you.'

Immediately, I thought of Vasant. He had made his life miserable by thinking about what he did not have, whereas this uneducated woman, Girija, had learnt to see the positive side of every difficulty and to enjoy life.

28

Light as Many Candles as Possible

I was travelling with my father in the interior parts of Karnataka, in the areas bordering Maharashtra. My father, a retired professor and doctor, used to guide my work and was my favourite companion on my travels. We were in a village where there was a famous temple dedicated to a goddess. It was a Friday, the auspicious day of the week for women all over India. Many women had come with offerings of fruit and flowers for the goddess. They had formed a long queue, but I was not part of it.

Having come to study the destitute in the area, I sat separately, talking to people. There were fruitsellers, bangle sellers and other vendors. I learned a lot from these people on the street. They had faced the harsh realities of caste, money, politics, old beliefs and much more. Their opinions and suggestions at times educated me better than any Ph.D thesis or seminar on poverty.

Once, I met a retired *gharwali* (commercial sex worker) along with a beautiful girl of sixteen who had long hair, a pretty face, beautiful eyes and a smooth complexion. Innocence added radiance to her face. She was wearing a green sari, green bangles and plenty of jasmine in her hair. The older woman claimed she was the young girl's aunt.

Though I was talking to the aunt, my eyes were fixed on the young girl. During the course of our discussion, I learned that this young girl had just become a *devadasi* (woman dedicated to the temple). There is a ban on converting women to *devadasis*, but many things happen illegally in our country.

I looked at the aunt. She was a *devadasi* too. She smelled strongly and had black teeth stained from chewing tobacco, a big paunch and red eyes. Her face bore a harsh, greedy expression. She was wearing a silk sari, gold bangles and a necklace. But no amount of gold could make her beautiful.

This young girl was going to be a gold mine for the old hag. I imagined that this girl of sixteen would probably become like her aunt after thirty years or so. Then she would also catch hold of some innocent girl, make her a *devadasi* and exploit her as a source of income. What a pity—the girl was not even aware of where she was heading.

Tears filled my eyes and suddenly I started sobbing uncontrollably. People standing around stared at me, wondering what had gone wrong. They probably thought that I had lost something. For the first time in my life, words failed to express my feelings. But my father immediately understood what was troubling me. He said, 'Tears cannot solve age-old problems. We can only try to reduce them. You cannot change the life of every single person. If you can rehabilitate ten such people in your lifetime, I will be a proud father. Proud that I have given birth to a daughter who could change the lives of ten helpless women.'

Everybody should know her own capacity and strength. One should also know one's own limitations. It is more difficult to recognize our weaknesses than our strengths. Don't aim for the sky. Keep your feet firmly on the ground and work around you. There is so much misery and gloom, but it is better to light a single candle than to remain in darkness. Try to light as many candles possible.

29

WOMAN WITH A MIND

My friend Nalini is a professor at a college in Bangalore. A Ph.D in history, she is a good teacher and an excellent wife. I had not met her for a long time, so one day I decided to visit her. She was excited to see me. She was cooking a special meal for her only son, who had returned from school. While her son was preparing for the 12th standard exams, her husband, Satish, an engineer in a multinational company, was away at work. So there was enough space and time for us to talk.

'I haven't seen you around at all, Nalini. What's new in life?'

'Nothing. I have been busy because Sameer is in the twelfth standard.'

'Come on, Nalini. You are not appearing for the exam. What you can do is help him at home, but that does not mean cutting yourself off from the world.'

Nalini did not agree. She was tense and worried.

'Nalini, what is the problem? Have you finished with the construction of your house?'

'Satish is looking after that.'

'You were planning to buy a new vehicle. What happened?'

'Yes. Satish is planning to buy a scooter rather than a car.'

I soon realized that all the decisions were Satish's. 'Nalini, don't you have any preferences?'

'Satish is better than me in all things. He knows the outside world and has lots of contacts. So his decisions will always be correct.'

I was surprised by her answer. Usually, educated, working women are more confident and independent, and they like to make their own decisions.

The next day, I was travelling to a village by bus. For a change, the bus was not crowded. A village woman, Yellamma, got into the bus along with me. I knew her because whenever I was in her village she would bring me fresh vegetables and refuse to accept money. Yellamma was around thirty-five, healthy and cheerful. Her well-oiled hair was tied in a knot and a thick black-bead *mangalsutra* rested on her neck. She also wore heavy gold ear studs, a big nose ring and more than a dozen green glass bangles on each wrist. No cosmetics and no pretence. Her pleasant smile added radiance to her glowing reddish-brown complexion. Yellamma and her husband, Rudrappa, owned a small garden in the village and that was their biggest asset. They grew and sold seasonal vegetables for a living.

'Amma, I have to rush back to my garden today,' she said.

'Why are you in such a hurry? Isn't your husband in the garden?' I asked.

'Yes. But still I must go because I have to take an important decision today. I have to sow the seeds ideal for the next three months.'

'Surely your husband can do that,' I suggested.

'No, I have to make my own decision. Rudrappa is also very good and experienced, but I should also give my views because not all seeds can be sown in the rainy season.'

I liked her confidence.

'Initially, when I gave my opinions, everyone used to laugh at me. I realized, however, that unless I became assertive, they would not give me any chance to make decisions. Without making decisions, I would not gain experience. So I started sowing vegetable seeds in one corner of the garden. Neither my mother-in-law nor my husband knew that place and I experimented. The first few times, they failed, but I didn't give up. Eventually I learnt which vegetables grew in which season. Today they respect my ideas and ask me to decide. This year, I want to plant carrots and cauliflower. I am sure that the yield will be good and fetch good money.'

Though uneducated and untrained, Yellamma was so different from Nalini.

30

THE IT DIVIDE

My friend Swapna had been unwell for three weeks, but I had come to know about her illness only after many days. After office one day, I thought of visiting her, though it was late afternoon. I wanted to take some fruit and flowers, but I was wondering where to buy them. Normally, my mother and sister do the shopping. I called my assistant, Ramesh, and asked him to show me where I could get good fruit and flowers. He knew of a shop that was on the way to Swapna's house and we decided to stop there to make my purchases.

It was one of those hot afternoons. I was nearly drenched in sweat and my cotton sari was crumpled. As I was going to meet a good friend, I wanted to choose the flowers myself, instead of leaving the choice to Ramesh.

At the shopping complex, the ice-cream stall appeared to be doing brisk business. I could see the rush of excited children and their worried mothers. Being holiday time, the children seemed totally unconcerned about their mothers' threats and warnings. It reminded me of the times when my children used to do the same and I felt sorry that those childhood days were gone.

I was now standing in front of the flower shop, which also sold fruit. The bright, colourful and fragrant flowers were arranged so well that it was hard to take my eyes off them. There were fragrant white rajnigandhas, bright red roses, gladioli in half bloom and many other kinds of flowers. They seemed to have just arrived from the garden, as their stems were still being trimmed and dipped in water.

On the other side were mounds of neatly arranged fruit: mangoes from Mumbai, grapes from Bijapur, guavas from Allahabad, oranges from Nagpur. They all looked so tempting that I was confused about what to buy. I asked the shopkeeper how much a bunch of pink roses would cost. They hadn't bloomed fully and looked very beautiful. Though he had heard me, he did not bother to answer. I repeated my question.

Disdainfully he answered, 'Each rose will cost Rs 3.50 and there are twenty roses to a bunch. That makes it Rs 70.'

I was taken aback. I had become like Rip Van Winkle. Unaware of the prevailing rates, I could recall only the old prices and felt that everything had become very expensive. I decided to enquire about the price of mangoes as well. I pointed to some Ratnagiri Alphonsos and asked him the cost of a dozen.

The irritable vendor answered, 'Rs 150 a dozen.' Then, speaking in Tamil, thinking I wouldn't understand, he remarked sarcastically to his friend, 'These people cannot afford anything but come shopping anyway. They are only window-shopping. I get tired of answering their questions. People who really want to buy don't ask the price.'

By this time, Ramesh had completed his shopping and came to the flower shop. Smart and well dressed at all times, he was wearing a T-shirt with the company logo and his employee card dangled around his neck. Now it was his turn to enquire about the price of the roses and the mangoes.

Looking at him or probably at his T-shirt, the shopkeeper replied politely, 'Sir, a bunch of those roses will cost you Rs 100. Only five rupees per flower. The actual price is Rs 150 but for you, I will give it at Rs 100. See these mangoes. They will cost only Rs 200.'

Ramesh didn't say anything, but I couldn't keep quiet.

'How can you demand such a price? Two minutes ago you were telling me that the roses and mangoes cost Rs 70 and Rs 150. Now you have increased the price. How can you do such a thing?'

The shopkeeper got angry. 'If you can't afford to buy, then keep quiet. Here is a man who is working for a big company. Can't you see his badge and company shirt? He is in a software company. They can afford any price and they don't bargain. People like you cause only headaches to us.'

Ramesh was about to reply, but I stopped him. It was a matter of great interest to me. I have heard many people, including real estate brokers, marriage brokers, landlords and job consultants, classify our company as a software company or an IT company. But this was more than all that.

'Is it really true that people working in IT companies have to pay different rates compared to ordinary people like us?' I asked.

'Yes. I am from Mangalore. I have seen that the moment

a man is working in an IT company, the dowry rises by at least two lakhs. After all, they do earn so much. What is wrong if I increase my price by just fifty rupees?'

Back in the car, I reflected on the digital divide-and-rule policy in operation for IT and non-IT workers, even in everyday life.

31

WHERE THERE'S A WILL . . .

Recently, I was invited to inaugurate a college auditorium. Though not large, the auditorium was well planned. After the inauguration, I was shown around the place. To my surprise, there was not even an inch of vacant space anywhere. All the walls were decorated with granite slabs and on every slab was inscribed the donors' names and the amounts they had donated. There was also a series of photographs on the wall. It all seemed a little odd.

The organizer noticed my expression and explained, 'Madam, we appealed to our donors for help in this work. Very few people came forward. Then we thought it over and decided to advertise that whoever donated more than Rs 1000 would have their name engraved on a granite slab on the wall. Whoever donated Rs 5000 and above would have their photos displayed on the wall.'

'What about those people who pay more than Rs 10,000?' I asked.

'Their names would be engraved on a separate marble stone and displayed at the entrance itself,' he replied. 'Just as we expected, we collected enough money to complete this project. There were even some strange donors who donated Rs 1000 four times so that their names could appear on four slabs on the wall!'

Yes, it is important to remember the person who has donated his hard-earned money, but not to this extent. My mind went back to a great personality who was far ahead of his time: Mariappa, a wealthy merchant from Bangalore, who first thought of doing philanthropic work in 1914. Though he was not educated, he was a great benefactor of poor students. He would provide them with food at his house and also take care of their fees.

He died on 12 March 1914, having written his will barely eight days earlier. In it, he bequeathed a monthly pension of Rs 60 to his wife till her death. The couple did not have children. He also arranged to supply oil and perform pujas in four temples in the city. He then specified that among the needy Hindu students, fifteen Nagaratha Lingayats, fifteen Brahmins and fifteen Hindus from other castes should be provided the facility of free boarding and lodging in Bangalore.

Not much is known about Mariappa's personal life. Probably, great philanthropists are introverted. They don't wish the whole world to know about their deeds. On the contrary, they believe that the *dana* given by the right hand should not be known even to the left hand.

It took almost seven years to liquidate Mariappa's assets. The money obtained was approximately Rs 1.45 lakh, which was a huge sum in those days. Half the money was spent on buying some land and constructing a hostel on it, while the remainder was kept as a corpus fund in the then newly started Mysore Bank. B.K. Mariappa Hostel, located on Chamarajapet, III Main, Bangalore, officially started on 1 July 1921 with forty-five poor and needy students from different castes. The Trust had six honorary trustees who were recognized as eminent people in public life.

Recently, the Mariappa Hostel celebrated its eightieth anniversary and also the 120th birth anniversary of its founder. This great philanthropist has helped educate many eminent people who have gone on to become famous in different walks of life. Without the gesture of this generous person, they probably would have faced great difficulty in completing their education.

32

CRISIS OF CONFIDENCE

Charu was one of my students who used to excel in her studies. She got a job in a bank, married an engineer and settled down happily. I used to meet her once in a while. Initially, she looked happy and radiant, but later, as time passed, she looked as though she carried a big burden. One morning, she came to my office. It surprised me because she would never disturb me in the mornings. I was sure something was wrong when she burst into tears on seeing me.

'Ma'am, I thought I could live happily once I chose my husband,' she said.

Apparently things hadn't turned out that way. After the first few days of love and care, Charu's husband and his mother began harassing her, forcing her to do all the housework in addition to her job at the bank. She had to hand over her entire salary to her husband and when she required any money—even ten rupees—she would have to ask him for it.

'As this marriage was against the wishes of my mother-in-law, she finds fault with everything I do,' said Charu. 'My husband, Suresh, is always a mother's son first, but never Charu's husband. I try to please them by doing whatever they tell me to do. But still they are unhappy with me.'

There are millions of Charus in our country who are well educated and hold good jobs. Once they are married, they have one problem or the other and they suffer throughout their lives. If providing education to women is empowerment, then why are so many women still crying? If economic independence is real independence, then why are they still suffering? This question always puzzles me. All these women are, by any standard, competent individuals. If such women suffer and shed tears, then what will happen to those young girls in the villages who are uneducated, economically dependent and who do not have any say about any aspect of their lives, be it buying clothes or choosing a husband? What could be the extent of their suffering?

As a teacher, I feel that apart from academics, it is very important to teach students the basic code of life. Many a time, my female students discuss marriage, money and careers. I always try to encourage the idea of self-reliance and confidence. It is important, particularly for the girls in our country, to have self-confidence. After all, getting married and raising children is not the ultimate aim of a woman. Education can, no doubt, fetch you good jobs. But more than that, one should be able to face life and its realities, and understand society.

Charu should have discussed her problems openly with her husband and mother-in-law and should have asserted her rights, but she was always submissive and wanted to please them. If you try to please everyone, you will please no one. It is impossible to lead your life for others' happiness. In any permanent relationship, it is wiser to put all your cards on the table, show how much you can change and how much you cannot.

Recently, I was invited to a function in Delhi. Its main theme was the empowerment of women and it was also an occasion where a few awards were being given away. One of the speakers was Kiran Bedi. I have always had a special appreciation and regard for Kiran because she symbolizes women with inner strength. It shows on her face also. Speaking extempore from her heart, forceful and sincere, she narrated the following incident.

A girl with a master's degree in business administration fell in love with her classmate and ran away to get married in a temple. There was no proof of their wedding other than a *mangalsutra* round her neck. No registration, no photo. After living together for a few days, the man abandoned her and this girl had to run from pillar to post for help.

Blaming the girl for being ignorant and finding the runaway husband were secondary to Kiran's fundamental question: what kind of education had this girl actually received? What was the use of all those years she had spent studying in school and college? A girl who was educated, who could lead an economically independent life but was now crying for help, was not a thing to be brushed aside, Kiran Bedi pointed out.

Education means more than scoring good marks in exams or receiving certificates. Life is an exam where the syllabus is unknown and question papers are not set. Nor are there model answer papers. There are various types of questions that can come from any direction, but one shouldn't run away. Education and financial independence are tools that can help us face difficulties, but confidence must be developed throughout life.

Life is a mixture of many kinds of people. I have seen some people always talking ill of others. Not that I am against people giving one another feedback. But such feedback should be constructive and help to improve oneself. Unfortunately, people can be remarkably insensitive and make comments that are in poor taste when they offer criticism.

Recently, a social worker received the Padmashree. He is a dedicated person and works selflessly; he truly deserved the award. But the comment that my friend Parvati made about him was horrible: 'Oh! He is a rich man. He must have spent a lot of money to buy the award. What else can he do with all his money? He donates some money and the Padmashree is awarded. If I had that kind of money, I would have got it much earlier. Besides, there is nothing great about a Padmashree. Can anybody remember who got it last year? Every year, hundreds of people get it; this year he got it.'

I have known Parvati for many years. Whenever somebody achieves something, her first reaction is negative. The reason is jealousy. She is so self-centred and insensitive that she is not bothered about what others think.

Manish, another friend's son, got the first rank in his degree examination. Naturally, his mother was thrilled. At the party, a gloomy-faced Parvati took me aside and said, 'Manish was not such a great student compared to my daughter, Mala. There must have been something wrong in the paper evaluation. What do you think, as a teacher?'

'You're wrong. Both Manish and Mala are good students. There is nothing wrong in the evaluation. He must have worked harder,' I said.

I met Parvati recently in the market.

'Who is your ghost writer?' she asked.

I was taken aback. 'Why should anybody write for me? I can write myself.'

'No, you hardly get any time, so I assumed that you must be hiring a writer, just as you hire a cook,' she said.

I was upset. How on earth could she talk like that? How could she assume such things? Without being in the least perturbed about having upset me, she delivered her parting shot before she walked away, 'Normally people do things like that, so I asked you.'

Parvati is an example of educated people who always comment on others. Their energy is spent in criticizing others. They always think that there is foul play in everything. We dream of so many things in life, but we may not be able to achieve them. Achievement is the product of many factors and not of hard work alone. One requires the right opportunity, the right people to work with and the right timing. Maybe there is an element of luck too.

An achiever has to work hard and have faith in his work. Often people work hard but do not achieve much. That doesn't mean they are any less than others who are more successful. If I am unable to realize my dream and somebody else does, it is better for me to feel happy for the other person than to feel sorry for myself. The best culture is one in which we rejoice in each other's success.

Today, nobody likes Parvati. She hardly has any friends. She feels that good things should happen to her alone, that she alone deserves the best in the world. Her world consists only of her family—her daughter, her son and her husband. Others do not exist for her.

What do such people achieve in life? No genuine friendship, no affection, no sharing. Is life worth living with this kind of jealousy?

THE TRUTH ABOUT WOMEN

When women in India won the right to vote, it was seen as a sign of equality and freedom. But, in reality, their social status is not good. That is why we see plenty of bride burnings, female infanticides and other atrocities committed against women.

Recently, I attended a seminar on women's issues. During the talks, something very interesting was read out. It was a list of countries where women enjoy freedom in all respects—economically, socially and politically. The countries where women were more emancipated featured at the top of the list while countries which lagged behind in empowering women came lower in the list. I assumed that India would feature somewhere in the middle of the list. In fact, it was the second-last country to be named. It came as a total surprise to me and, of course, a bitter one.

I was curious to know which were the first three countries. I expected England or America to be at the top of the list. I was wrong again. The top three countries were all Scandinavian: Sweden, Norway and Denmark. Most of us at the seminar were taken aback. We were surprised that such small countries lying in a corner of Europe were the countries that respect their women the most.

Once, on a visit to Stockholm, I was late in returning to my hotel one night. As I was quite far from the hotel, I had to take a taxi. The fare to the hotel was 40 kronor, but thinking that the taxi driver would charge at least double considering the late hour, I gave him 100 kronor and waited for the change. He returned 80 kronor.

When I asked why, he said, 'You are a lady travelling at this hour of the night, so we take only half of the actual fare.'

I was really impressed. Back home in my country, I would not even dare to travel after dark. Even if I did, the taxi driver would surely charge me multiples of the actual fare.

We talk endlessly on the podium. We worship goddesses. We are proud to say that women have the same rights as men in our constitution. The Ardhanareeshwara form of Lord Shiva shows that he too had consented to this equality. Our scriptures and our history tell of women with extraordinary qualities. But, in reality, do our women really feel secure? Do they actually enjoy freedom? Do they enjoy equal rights in society? Maybe a few do.

Women are usually identified in relation to men—as a daughter, a wife or a mother. Often, Indian women do not have a say even in personal matters. Their services are not rewarded nor is their efficiency appreciated. They have to live in a male-dominated society. It is ridiculous that often those of their own gender are their worst enemies. It is a different matter, a matter of pride, that the Indian woman has learnt to live and excel in such an environment.

In contrast, women are respected in the three Scandinavian countries. We just talk, but they practise. The saying, 'Where women are happy, the goddess dwells,' holds true only in such places.

Not all that glitters is gold. Not all that is white is milk. Not all people who wear saffron clothes are sages. These age-old sayings hold true even now, especially the last one. We see a lot of people wearing saffron clothes, but not all of them are *sanyasis* in the true sense of the word. A *sanyasi* is one who guides his followers on the right path.

Recently, I attended the inaugural function of a home for destitute women in Mysore. In most cases, the women were there because they were either harassed by their in-laws or tortured by drunken husbands. Owing to their socio-economic conditions, even the parents of the victims were unable to take them in and care for their hapless children. There had also been instances when young girls, lured by romance, had run away from their homes and had been deserted by their lovers after the honeymoon. These girls usually did not dare return to their parents.

The saying that 'success has many fathers, but failure has none' is true indeed. We get to see only the distressed women and their children, while the main cause of their problems remains hidden in the background. So the victims cannot be blamed altogether. Often it is circumstances that force them into such drudgery. These women and girls need to be psychologically strong and determined to face difficulties with courage and go on with their lives. The more unfortunate ones may get caught in the ugly network of commercial sex or other unlawful activities, either knowingly or unknowingly.

It is nice to respect or reward people who work for such women. More importantly, it is also necessary to lend a helping hand to those who have stumbled or lost their way. Do we have such a system? There are very few institutions where such people are given shelter and efforts made to rehabilitate them. In such institutions, women are taught how to earn a livelihood so that they can live with dignity.

In Mysore, the first person who came up with the idea to open such an institution was not someone who had political powers or wanted fame. He is the head of the Suttur *math*. The swamiji is well read and felt the need to help the downtrodden and destitute, having truly understood the meaning of compassion.

He could have led a quiet life, performing his religious duties and looking after his own *math*, but he thought of something different. The swamiji gave a donation worth Rs 1 crore in the form of one-and-a-half acres of land belonging to his *math*. He showed the true nature of a leader, exemplary in his behaviour. It is a matter to be highlighted that he did all this without any expectation of a return. *Acharya devo bhava*, say our ancestors, implying that the guru or the teacher is equal to God. How truly the actions of the swamiji of the Suttur *math* reflect this saying!

Whenever I write a column, I give my email address to enable readers to express their views on the article. I also add a sentence reminding them that their emails should be regarding the column only. However, I do get plenty of emails about things other than the column. Some emails appreciate the contents of the column, but some of them are sarcastic.

The column 'Last Word', which I have been writing for a while, is my personal opinion and is naturally highly subjective. As far as possible, I try to convey to the readers what is on my mind. It is very easy to narrate the horrors of dowry death, the causes of corruption or moralize on the virtue of honesty and so on. Anyone can preach, for that matter. But most of the readers ask me to narrate something personal that happened to me or to someone in my circle of friends. As a teacher, I am always aware that analogies and examples make the subject clearer. So, when I write I narrate some of my experiences. The incidents might have happened in my own family or among my friends. But it is not to highlight what my son said or how my friend spoke. I write only to share those few everyday moments, something that my readers can identify with. But I have come across many readers who misunderstand this and waste their time sending some critical and hurtful emails.

I got a letter after I wrote 'Not all's wrong with the next generation'. I was describing a conversation with my son. The purpose of the article was not to glorify either my son or myself. It was a conversation between two generations, my son representing the next generation and I, my own generation. I could have written the conversation more impersonally as one which took place between Mister A and Mrs B or just as an objective essay making generalizations on the generation gap. But I felt it was better to write about something that had really happened. However, the response I got for this was the accusation, 'You write about your son.'

Once, I wrote about social insensitivity. My aim was to tell others how much we are insulated in our own world, with no time at all to know or care about what is happening around us. We must definitely care for our families and I don't deny that. Family is important and one should not become a philanthropist at the cost of one's family. My concern was that we should at least think of other people. I did not mean it was necessary to offer financial help or give money. I gave a small example from my experience. But some readers were critical about my narrating a story and praising Buddha. Lord Buddha, in my article, symbolized the ultimate sacrifice of a sensitive person who went on to help others. Everyone cannot be Buddha, but at least we can think and learn from such great people.

When my articles end on a positive note, they are

popular with readers. But the moment an article ends on a negative note, I get letters saying, 'We never expected such a thing from you,' or 'You should always write good things.' In real life, no human being has all good qualities, no human being has been successful in every aspect of life, no system is without its negatives. In reality, life is a mixture of plus and minus, joy and sorrow, ups and downs. It is the duty of a writer to portray that the negative is also a part of life and that we should accept it as such while also thinking positively.

The same incident can be viewed from two different angles by two different people. In my column, I try my level best to show my sincere feeling towards issues of common concern. My aim is not to show off or describe anything personal. I just want to narrate an incident and let readers think about it in relation to their own lives. Unbiased inputs from the readers help me to think and improve myself in my personal column.

Neither the money I earn from writing nor the desire for fame makes me write. I just have the urge to share my vast experience of meeting people, trying to understand them and realizing what life is all about. Many times, people act impulsively due to emotions like greed or jealousy. That doesn't mean they are bad. These are also the qualities of a human being. That's why I believe that readers are the source of my inspiration.

Recently, I wrote a column about the century's greatest idea—the idea of non-violence, conceived by our own leader, Mahatma Gandhi. By following the ideal of non-violence, three people were awarded the Nobel Prize for peace. They were Martin Luther King Jr, Nelson Mandela and Aung San Suu Kyi of Myanmar. Martin Luther King, in particular, when he received the Nobel Prize at Oslo in Norway, described and praised Mahatma Gandhi and declared that he would follow the path of non-violence in the violent country of America. Ironically, Gandhi himself never received the Nobel Prize.

When I wrote this article, one of the readers sarcastically wrote, 'It was good that Mr M.K. Gandhi did not get the Nobel Prize because after all it was instituted by the Dynamite King.'

What a wrong way to think of Alfred Nobel! He probably was the first philanthropist who thought of the entire globe as his own village. He was truly an international man, as early as a century ago. In 1896, when he wrote his will, he probably would never have dreamt that he was creating a new idea of philanthropy. The recipients of his award are international. Incidentally, seven hundred Nobel Prizes have been given in the last one hundred years. Nobel never gave away any of these prizes in his lifetime. Though the will was written in 1896, the first prizes were given only in 1901. Very few Swedes have received the Nobel Prize. But the people who receive them are, by and large, respected throughout the world.

A reader's question, 'What's great about Nobel?' prompted me to write about the Nobel Prize. Why did Nobel give away all his property, approximately three million dollars in those days, to charity? He could have given his vast estates to his relatives or to a religious society or to his countrymen. What made him institute prizes for literature, peace, physics, chemistry and medicine? He might have earned money from dynamite, but that doesn't mean he was fond of war.

A knife is very essential in the kitchen, but it can also be a horrible weapon that can take life. It depends on who wields it. Western Europe and America are very grateful to Nobel because he invented dynamite. Dynamite helped build the railways by cutting through mountains and making tunnels. Railways connect people. But if somebody used the railways for war, it was not Nobel's fault.

It seems Nobel never liked propaganda or any publicity. Very few photographs of him can be seen in the Nobel Museum. He was a great achiever. Whatever he did, he did well, be it business or philanthropy. Nobel, as a person, was shy and a peace lover. This is evident in his will. He clearly writes, 'Anything for the betterment of the human race should be respected and awarded, so that the person will not have any financial difficulties in achieving his goals.'

It is very interesting to note that very few women have been awarded the Nobel Prize, particularly in science. The reason is that very few countries encourage women's education. Most of the time, Americans and Europeans have won the award. The reason is the expensive infrastructure for research in science that exists in these countries.

It is not necessary that the Nobel Prize be awarded in the specified field every year. If the Nobel Committee does not find the right candidate one year, then the Nobel Prize in that field is not awarded. Jean Paul Sartre, a famous French writer, rejected the Nobel Prize. Madame Curie was awarded it twice; her daughter, Irine, received it once in chemistry and another daughter, Eva, representing UNESCO, also received this award. Probably this is the only case in history where all members of the same family received the award.

Nobel sowed the seed of 'helping mankind'. Then in the early part of 1910, Rockefeller and later Ford started their foundations. Today, there are many prizes all over the world for various activities. But Nobel remains as strong as the Himalaya in his deed and symbolizes the love for peace and mankind.

38

UNWED MOTHERS

A few years ago, I was a counsellor to students. That was the time when I came to know about the problems faced by teenagers, particularly girls. Normally, girls are shy and parents expect 100 per cent obedience from them. One of my students, Kusuma, had become pregnant before marriage. The boy was her classmate, but he was not brave enough to marry her. When her parents came to know about it, they were very upset. When they met me, the first thing they said was, 'What will others think? How will we face society?' The boy's parents were not prepared for this marriage. Ultimately, the girl committed suicide.

I felt extremely sad and helpless. For the first time, I recognized the problems of unwed mothers in our society. In real life, the pressure on the girl and the family is enormous.

Recently, I visited Norway. A Norwegian friend, Martha, took me to her house for a meal. Hers was a simple middle-class family. Martha was an only daughter and both her parents were teachers. She was also a teacher in a high school.

It was summer and around 8 p.m. The sun was shining like it was 2 p.m. in the afternoon. Isn't that the reason

Norway is called the land of the midnight sun? The house was simple and sparkling. Everyone at dinner knew English, which was of great help to me. Simple vegetarian fare was served at the table. A little boy of five came running in and hugged Martha. He was very naughty and yet innocent and lovable. He sat next to me in a high chair.

After some time, Martha's cousin, Mary, joined us for dinner. The conversation was casual. Mary was a postgraduate student in political science. While I was talking to her about the political conditions in Norway, the little boy pulled Mary's skirt and said, 'Mom, I want more bread.'

I was surprised to hear that. Mary was a young girl of about twenty-four; she seemed too young to have such a grown-up son. During the conversation, I asked Mary where her husband was working. Without any guilt or shyness she replied, 'I am not married. But John is my son. I am an unwed mother.'

I could not believe this. Here was a woman who had a son out of wedlock and announced it without hesitation. And he was accepted by the family, too.

After dinner, Martha came to drop me. I could not resist the temptation and asked her, 'Tell me, Martha, if you don't mind, is Mary happy? What do her parents feel? Where is the boy's father? I just want to know because of my student back home.'

I explained Kusuma's story to her. Martha was distressed to hear the sad story and replied, 'Mary met Daniel at a summer camp when they were both just eighteen years old. He used to come and visit us often. They fell in love and she became pregnant by mistake. Sex education is given to us at school, but mistakes still happen. When Mary got pregnant, Daniel did not want to marry her because he was also in college. Moreover, they figured that their temperaments were too different. Even if they had married, it would have ended in divorce. They decided to separate. Mary felt that she could continue with her pregnancy. She never wanted to have an abortion, so she gave birth to the baby. She nursed him for a year and now is back at college. She may marry her new boyfriend next year.'

For me, there were thousands of questions to ask. What was the reaction of Mary's parents? Did John know his father? Where was Daniel? And so on.

Martha probably sensed my curiosity and explained, 'My uncle and aunt did not worry because it was Mary's decision and there are many unwed mothers in our country. Daniel has a good job and visits John twice a year. He pays money for the child's maintenance and he too may marry his new girlfriend in the new year. John knows about it. Mary is not upset with Daniel.' My thoughts drifted back to my student, Kusuma, and her death. Same situation, probably at a similar age, but the outcome was so different. Mary looks confident and happy whereas poor Kusuma is dead.

39

Alliances Invited

Time and tide wait for no one. This is really true. A quarter of a century ago, we used to attend our friends' weddings. Now we attend their children's weddings.

I attended Vani's marriage. Her mother Vanita is a friend of mine. I distinctly remember Vanita's own wedding. Her marriage was finalized through an advertisement placed by her father in the matrimonial column of the *Hindu*, thirty years ago. Matrimonial advertisements were something new in those days. Normally, matches were made through personal contacts. Advertising in a paper was the last resort. Vanita was a tall girl. Finding a boy taller than her in our small circle was not easy, so her father had to resort to advertising.

I still remember the advertisement. 'Alliance invited for a tall, 24-year, from a traditional family, Smarta, Athreya Gothra, Ashwini Nakshatra Prathama Charana girl, a commerce graduate, bank employee. Knows all household work, excellent in a joint family, ready to work or stay at home after marriage. Knows good embroidery and knitting. Tall grooms aged 29 yrs to 34 yrs, above 5.8", from the same community, with horoscope, through their parents, from good family, should apply. Groom should be at least a graduate. Working in Bank/Govt/ Public sector is preferable. A good wedding is assured. Apply to Box No. xxx.'

Vanita got a husband who was working as an engineer in a public-sector company. He was from a joint family and belonged to the same community. Her father-in-law demanded twenty sovereigns of gold, five silk saris, a suit for the boy, to-and-fro bus charges for the entire marriage party and a good three-day wedding. Though it was difficult for them, Vanita's family agreed.

The wedding preparations were enormous and time-consuming. As she was the first girl in our group to get married, we too were involved in the preparations. We accompanied her to select saris and jewellery. Elders at home were busy arranging for cooks and varieties of sweets.

Now, years later, at the wedding lunch of Vanita's daughter, I saw the new couple, Vani and her husband, happily chatting away as if they had known each other for a long time. Caterers were very busy arranging different kinds of food. Tired but happy, Vanita came and sat next to me.

My mind went back to the days of Vanita's wedding. Because I knew all the details of her marriage and because her daughter's marriage had happened so suddenly, I asked for details.

Vanita smiled and replied, 'Oh! It was just like mine. An advertisement in the *Hindu* matrimonial column. But the kind of ad was different.'

It was a hot May day. Wiping the perspiration with

her silk sari, Vanita opened her purse and showed me the paper cutting. She said, 'I am going to attach this to Vani's wedding album.'

I read the ad. 'Alliance invited for a smart, slim, fair, 22-yr-old software engineer, from a modern family, preferring to stay overseas. The girl is convent educated and prefers nuclear family. Outgoing and Karate Black Belt. Enjoys Western music and travelling. Handsome boys between 22-25 yrs, well connected, well settled, preferably a software/MNC, small family, can apply directly. Horoscope not needed. Caste no bar.'

Vanita then explained how her daughter's marriage had been fixed in a week's time, without hassle or tension. Vani received about one hundred applications from all over, but only five were short-listed. She met all the five boys separately; two did not approve of her and she did not like another two. Thus, the final choice was made. This boy was working in the US as a software engineer. Vani's passport had been readied when she was in her final year. She had got a job in a software company. She knew that she had to marry soon so she learnt driving, swimming, aerobics, nutrition and diet.

'Does she know cooking?' I asked, since Vani was going to live abroad.

'Not needed. But she knows how to make pasta, soup, noodles and pizzas. Anyway the market is flooded with ready-to-use mixes. She can manage the kitchen with all these things.'

'Did you buy a lot of jewellery and saris?'

'No. Nowadays the in-laws don't demand jewellery or

a dowry. Instead, they want the first-time airfare to the US for the bride. My daughter does not want to buy many saris either. She hardly wears them and feels it will be a waste. So she bought just two saris, six salwar kameez sets and ten sets of Western clothes, which are more useful to her. And we made lightweight jewellery.'

I was amazed at how times have changed. Traditional matrimonial columns show the change even in arranged marriages. Change is very essential in life. Depending on the circumstances, rituals and people change. Is it not true that nothing is constant in life except change?

Recently, I was in a selection committee to recruit a software engineer for a small firm. There were many young girls and boys anxiously awaiting their turn. They were all in the age group of twenty-one to twenty-four. It was probably the first interview for many of them and they looked tense. They were all computer science graduates, so I was sure that their technical knowledge would be sound.

It was the turn of a young boy. He was well mannered and as soon as he entered the room, he produced his certificates. The topmost one attested to his knowledge of Java, GW Basic, C++, etc.

I casually asked him how much time he would require to learn a new computer language.

'Not more than six months,' he replied.

Suddenly, my mind flashed back to a quarter-century earlier. I had met a young man of the same age as this boy in a similar situation and had asked him a similar question. But the answer I had received was so different. The young boy then had answered with confidence: 'I don't know anything about computers or their language. But give me four months' time. I will try to understand computers and I will come back to tell you how much time I require to learn the language.'

I was bowled over by his confidence and his straightforwardness. I still remember the whole scene vividly.

That was in Bombay. I was on an overview panel and this young man, who was basically a civil engineer, had come for the interview. It was for the post of a software engineer. Many people had done well in the interview. He was the last candidate to appear. He entered the interview room with a very clear mind and was very frank. He was given a logic test, not related to computers, and he solved it quickly. He made it clear that he had no computer background but that he was ready to learn and if found good, hoped to be given the job.

He got the job, worked relentlessly and came back saying, 'Give me any language. I will learn it in ten days. I will master it. Computer language is just a tool. The essence of programming is logic. One requires good logic, and that I have mastered.'

Over a period of time he did master many languages and became one of the most successful programmers I know. Though he was a junior, most of his seniors, including me, would ask for his opinion. He would do a lot more homework on the desk than on the system and once he started programming there would never be a single bug.

Whenever a youngster talks about computers, I am reminded of this young man with his admirable willingness to learn and frankness in accepting things. I pray that all our colleges produce more students like him.

41

SORRY, THE LINE IS BUSY

Rakesh and I had been classmates from school to college. He had become a part of our family and I of his. Later on, as we grew older, we chose different professions, parted and settled. He had his family and I had my own and we were immersed in our own worlds. In spite of being in the same city, we hardly met, though we really would have liked to meet often.

I thought of Rakesh on his birthday and wanted to greet him, but his telephone lines were busy from morning. Maybe, since it was his birthday, everybody wanted to wish him, so I decided to call him later in the day. Still, I had no luck. His lines remained busy. Now I thought his phones were off the hook. Even when I called him late at night, I could not get through. His lines must be out of order, I concluded.

After a month I met Rakesh at a party. He commented ironically that I was too busy to call a friend on his birthday. I defended myself saying that I had called him but his lines were perpetually busy. He was taken aback.

'Telephones are so unreliable. Always some repair or the other and lines are always out of order.'

Tara, Rakesh's very sensible wife, interrupted our conversation. 'Don't blame the telephone department. The problem lies in our house.'

I was surprised by her comment. 'Is there anything wrong at home?'

'Yes! I have two teenage children. And at any point of time when we want to use the telephone, those two are keeping both lines busy.'

'Surely not for the whole day!'

'Yes, for the whole day. They have parallel lines in their rooms. Material affluence has spoiled our normal living.'

I could make out that she was quite upset.

'All of us have one or two children and we pamper them,' she continued. 'Look at my daughters. They have separate rooms. There are two telephones and these girls use the telephones like we use water.'

'What are your telephone bills like?' My math-oriented mind thought of that.

'Who is worried about bills? Telephone bills are paid by the company. The children know that it's a perk given by all corporate houses. And cost is also not an important factor for them. My worry is about the constant conversation with friends. They solve their maths problems on the telephone. They share jokes on the telephone. They read books on the telephone.'

'Really? I have never heard of that!' Rakesh showed his ignorance of what went on in his house.

'Yes,' Tara went on. 'Normally they talk loudly, but when they are on the telephone their voices are almost like a whisper. One has to make an effort to hear what they're saying.'

'What happens if you lock up the telephone?' I suggested.

'It's of no use. Their friends will call our house and the telephone lines will be just as busy.'

'What do they do at night?'

'This computer chat takes up the remaining time. They connect to the Internet and that's it. Whatever you say, they do not understand.'

'Too much is too bad,' Tara continued. 'Telephones are used for communication, but when we do not get to use it even in an emergency, I feel frustrated. Today's children abuse the resources available to them. They do not know how to control their wants and desires,' concluded Tara, sighing with unhappiness.

I'm sure there are many Taras among us. Times have changed, but what Tara says is valid. The next generation will not understand that their elders advise them from experience. Probably these children will only realize the value of good advice when they become parents themselves and their children do not listen to them.

42

BE FAIR TO OTHERS

Once my aunt took me to her ladies' club to preside over a function. There was a delay due to some miscommunication among the organizers, so I was made to wait in the antechamber, where I couldn't do anything but observe the people around. I often feel that studying people's behaviour is more interesting than reading a book.

The ladies' club is in a posh area of Bangalore and is considered an elite institution. The members are mostly from the upper middle-class and most of them are well settled and well travelled. They were busy conversing about all the topics under the sun, from silk saris to the most recent English film in the town. My aunt was talking to her friend, Shanta, and they were engrossed in conversation. My aunt's voice was a little loud and though I was seated at a distance I could hear her conversation quite clearly.

'It is really wrong on your daughter-in-law's part,' my aunt declared like a Supreme Court judge. She was confident that her judgement was perfect, but she dragged me into the conversation anyway, just to get my opinion. 'Be fair. Is it correct on her part to behave like that?'

'Who is she?'

'Shanta's daughter-in-law, Rashmi. She wants an easy

life and loves to relax in far-off places during the school holidays.'

I looked so confused that my aunt decided to give me a brief history of the problem. 'Rashmi's in-laws, that is Shanta's family, are rich. They earned their wealth through hard work. Rashmi hails from an ordinary middle-class family and she loves to enjoy the money that she never earned. She wants to buy new clothes every month. As soon as her husband comes home, she wants to go out for a film or somewhere else. She gets up late in the morning . . .' The list of complaints was never-ending.

I suddenly thought of Radhika, my cousin, the daughter of the same aunt. Radhika too was married into a wealthy business family. Radhika was a schoolteacher and quite used to working very hard. After her marriage, I had met her at my place once. I could not believe what I saw. She had bloated up like a balloon. She was dressed in an expensive sari and decked with ornaments.

Radhika explained her daily routine to me. 'I get up in the morning around nine.'

'Why so late?'

'We have plenty of servants at home. They do all the work. Why should I get up so early? I worked a lot before marriage. Mahesh is very busy so I wait for his arrival from office. As soon as he comes, I want to go out for a film or a walk. I have not seen much of the world and managing two kids for the whole year is tiring. I've told Mahesh that we should go abroad for every holiday. Let it be Nepal or Sri Lanka, but I want to travel abroad during the school holidays.'

Thinking of what Radhika had said, I interrupted my aunt's complaints to ask, 'How is Radhika?'

'She's fine. Poor child. Her mother-in-law is a nagging type. She comments on everything. She is lucky to have a daughter-in-law like Radhika. If her mother-in-law had a daughter-in-law like Rashmi, then she would appreciate my daughter's worth.'

I felt depressed. These elderly women, despite being educated, were behaving like kindergarten children. What one's daughter does is all right but when a daughter-in-law does the same thing, then everything is wrong. The yardsticks are different because one is your daughter and the other is somebody else's daughter.

All this time I had been wondering what I should talk about to the gathering. At times, I feel at a loss because I don't know what topic will be of interest to the audience. Now I had decided—I would speak on the topic 'Be fair to others'.

43

BONDED BY BISLERI

The 26 January horror of Kutch in Gujarat is well known. Without any warning, Mother Earth opened her mouth and engulfed the people and their belongings. Overnight, rich people were reduced to the streets. But the spirit of the Kutchi people is admirable. They faced this disaster bravely and are still fighting to restore life to normalcy.

The media has to be congratulated for its role in the relief efforts. Within hours of the tragedy, all newspapers and television channels had zoomed in to cover the disaster and broadcast it all over the world. Along with India, the rest of the world participated in helping these unfortunate people. After all the rush of the TV crews and media people, hordes of NGOs and government officials landed up in Kutch. People started picking up their life from where they had left it. Life started to return to normal at a slow pace.

I went to visit these areas after some time, when the dust of propaganda had settled down, in order to see actual life. After all, the emotions had drained off and reality had become the priority.

Several small villages deep inside Kutch, away from the main road connecting Ahmedabad and Bhuj, had been badly affected by the earthquake. I was visiting these remote places in the deep interior when one of the tyres of my jeep went flat. Getting it fixed would take some time. My driver went to get this done.

I was alone and bored. I saw a few tents nearby. They were temporary sheds covered with blue plastic sheets. They were the temporary houses, schools and health centres for the people residing in that area. Later, I heard that there were tent hotels as well.

Life was busy and people were getting on with their chores. As it was monsoon season, men and women were busy in the fields. It was very strange. For many years there had not been much rain in Kutch, but that year it had rained abundantly. Farmers were having a bumper crop. I suppose nature has its own method of justice. On the one hand she takes away something and on the other she gives something in return. Small children were playing in the dust happily.

I peeped into one of the nearby tents. A young girl, about fourteen years old, was cleaning grains and preparing to cook a meal. When she saw me, she rose with a smile and said, 'Please come in and sit down.'

As I wanted to see how they lived, I entered the shed. She gave me a charpoy to sit on. Inside the tent it was clean and neat. There was a thin partition made of an old sari. I understood from her conversation that her family was not from Kutch.

The girl offered me a glass of water. Though it was the monsoon season, the sun was hot, but I was a little hesitant to drink the water. Many thoughts flashed across my mind. If the water was not sterile, then I was at risk of contracting diseases like dysentery, hepatitis B and jaundice. If I refused to accept the water, however, I knew I would hurt the girl's feelings. So I took the glass but did not drink the water.

The girl had a younger sister who might have been around twelve years old. There was a little boy sleeping in a home-made cradle. Outside, there was a temporary open kitchen where *sabzi* was being cooked. The elder one was making a dough of wheat flour.

'It seems from your language that you are not Gujaratis. Where are you from?' I asked.

Smiling, the younger sister answered, 'We're not from Gujarat, we're from Mumbai.'

'Have you come here to visit your relatives?'

'No, we don't have any relatives here. This is our house. We have come here with our parents.'

I was very surprised by this answer because, normally, people flee areas afflicted by calamities, whereas these people had moved in. 'What is your father doing here?'

Both girls were eager to give me information. The elder one replied, 'My father used to beg in Mumbai at Mahim Creek, near the church. My mother used to sell candles at the church entrance.'

'What made you come here?'

'One day, we saw the news on TV and we came to know that there had been an earthquake here. It was shown every hour on TV in the corner shop. My father said "Let's go" and we came here.'

'Who paid for your train tickets?'

'Nobody. We came here without tickets. The whole

train was full of people. There were many people like us who have come. The entire station was heavily crowded. There was no ticket collector.'

'How did you come from the train station?'

'We didn't know anyone. But there were plenty of buses running between the station and Bhuj. There were many foreign volunteers. The buses were jam-packed. We also got into one of the buses and landed on the main road.'

'How did you come to this particular area?'

'There were many jeeps going from the main roads to all interior villages. On the main road, there was a convoy of trucks full of different relief materials. They used to unload materials on either side of the road. People who did not have anything would pick them up from the roadside. We also picked up some.'

'What were the materials on the roadside?'

'There were food articles, apples, biscuit packets, clothes, blankets and many more items. My father told each one of us to pick up what we could and we collected a lot. We have never seen so much in our life in Mumbai. Everything was in plenty.'

Children are innocent and they always tell the truth until they become adults and lies creep into their lives. One lies to boast, to show what he is not. But children are so confident. They never pretend to be what they're not. Naturally, the Mumbai beggar's daughters described the whole scenario as if it was a very memorable event.

The elder one said much more than that. 'There were people crying, some of them in pain. Some had lost their children or parents. It was very sad to see. But there were plenty of people to help also. There were doctors working overnight. There were swamijis working like common men, distributing medicines. There were army people digging to build houses. There was no difference between day and night, the rich and the poor.

'Our position was better. We did not lose anybody, nor did we lose any material, because we never had anything to begin with. People who have something have to fear losing it, but people who don't have anything to lose have no such fear. My mother and father helped people and someone said that inside the villages there was nobody to help. There were jeeps constantly travelling between the villages and the main road. So we got into one of the jeeps and landed in this village. Some organization was giving bamboo, camping materials like tents, and other roofing materials, free to all those people who had lost their houses. As we had no home, we also got all the materials. Sometimes we got double because my mother was in one queue and my father in another.'

'What all have you got?'

'Plenty of food. We have been eating to our hearts' content every day and we have also been giving some to people who were unable to stand in the queue. We know what it is to be hungry.'

'Why did you settle here then?'

'My father had asthma in Mumbai. He was unable to breathe and on many days we would go hungry. Someone said it was due to the pollution. It might be true, because after we came here, he has been normal, because there's no pollution here. Anyway, we had also built our own house, so we decided to settle down.'

'What job does your father do here? Does he continue to beg?'

'No. We are self-sufficient now. He is working as a coolie in a nearby field. He earns Rs 100 a day. Our mother also does the same thing, so the income is doubled. We're comfortable. The earthquake has come like a boon to us.'

She asked her sister to get some tea and biscuits. She inquired, 'Which biscuits do you want?'

'Do you have a variety?' I asked, surprised.

She pulled the curtain aside and I was amazed to see the varieties of biscuit packets, cartons of Bisleri mineral water, utensils, steel trunks and other things.

'From the day of earthquake, most of us here have been drinking only Bisleri water. It seems some foreign country has sent a shipful of it. What I have given you is also mineral water.'

I drank the water with contentment.

44

BAHUT KUCH HOTA HAI

One Sunday morning I had an unusual visitor. He was a close friend from my childhood days and had also been our neighbour then. We had not met in thirty-five years. Suddenly, he appeared with his son, without any prior notice. Thirty-five years is a long time and much had happened since we last met. The young, handsome teenager I had known then now looked short, tired, with a bald head and a paunch. The confident, talkative person had become a little diffident, anxious and hesitant. I wonder how I appeared to him.

I was very happy to see him. We had great times as children. At the back of my mind, I remembered those carefree days. No wonder the words of the beautiful ghazal sung by Chitra and Jagjeet Singh, '*woh kagaz ki kashti woh baarish ka paani . . .*' bring tears to our eyes at times.

My friend introduced his son to me. He was a young man of twenty-two years with a bachelor's degree in electrical engineering. He looked indifferent and was not interested in our talk. I casually asked him what he was doing.

He perked up. 'I want to join a software company and then go to America. I want to stay there for five years and come back and start my own company and become big. I know that with ten thousand rupees one can build an empire. Is it not true, Aunty?'

I didn't know what to answer, because starting a company means a lot of struggle and hard work, and success is unpredictable. 'Where are you working now?'

'I am not working anywhere. I am waiting to join a good software company.'

'Do you have a background in programming or any experience?'

'No, I don't, but I'm sure that I will learn fast. I don't want to take up any other job now. If I take up a non-software job, I will get a salary of only five or six thousand rupees and I will have to be on the site too. It's not at all big money, so I haven't taken up anything.'

Now I understood the anxiety on my friend's pale face. He was about to retire and here was his son, unemployed and dreaming big. Dreaming is always good, but turning the dream into reality is more important. I remembered the words of TISCO chairman, J.J. Irani: 'Vision without action is merely a dream; action without vision is merely passing time; but vision and action together can change the world.'

As a teacher, I am used to giving advice. So, whether he liked it or not and whether he had asked for it or not, I gave him a piece of my mind. When he left with his father, his face was glum.

I could not help recalling the laziness and conceit of this young man when I met a boy with a totally different attitude some time later, on a beach in Orissa. Because

Orissa is blessed with both nature's beauty and magnificent examples of our nation's cultural heritage, most of us know only of the state's famous tourist attractions. There is a place, however, that is not as well known yet extremely beautiful. It is a small sleepy town of fishermen known as Chandipur, facing the Bay of Bengal. It is approximately 200 km from Bhubaneswar by road. It has a small guesthouse, but few visitors come here. Those who do make it this far are treated to a game of hide-and-seek with the sea. The unusual phenomenon is that at low tide the sea retreats a good five kilometres and the water disappears completely, revealing a stretch of flat land. One can walk, play or even drive a jeep on this temporary land. After a few hours, the sea comes back in full swing, as if nothing has happened. Visitors wait on the seashore to see this wonder. It's an amazing sight.

Once I was waiting on the seashore for the sea to recede in order to walk on the tidal plain. The sea was retreating slowly, but it hadn't receded far enough to walk. There were many fisherfolk on the shore, busy with their work. Whenever the sea starts to ebb, red crabs come out on the sand. Older children were busy collecting them and younger ones were collecting shells. The lean, dark and rugged fisherwomen, dressed in saris, were spreading their nets to catch fish. Then I saw a young boy of maybe twelve helping his mother to hold the net. When she became tired, he would help her, and when she did not need him, he would collect crabs. His actions showed that he was enthusiastic and happy. When he came to the shore, he approached me and offered me fresh crabs, perhaps thinking I was a prospective buyer. I said that I didn't eat crabs but that I wanted to talk to him.

He came and sat with me on some steps specially made for visitors. I looked at him carefully. He was thin and dark, but his eyes were like diamonds sparkling at night. He was wearing only shorts and his body was completely wet, but he did not seem uncomfortable or self-conscious. He was as natural as a fresh flower. His smile and enthusiasm were contagious.

I asked about his family. I came to know that his father was a rickshaw driver, earning fifty rupees a day. His mother supplemented the family income by catching fish and crabs. The boy, whose name was Javed, was studying in school and always stood first. He also had a little sister at home. I was curious to know how much Javed earned every day and also his schedule.

He said, 'In the morning, when the sea goes back, I hunt for crabs, help my mother and then go home, take a bath and do a little kitchen work to reduce my mother's burden. Then I go to school. Evenings, I do my homework and in the night, when the sea goes back, I go crab hunting again. Allah is very kind to our land. I heard that this is the only place in our country where the sea disappears and we can get crabs twice a day without much difficulty.' He probably earned five or ten rupees a day.

I was unhappy that he earned so little for such hard work. I asked him, 'Only five or ten rupees, Javed? What will you get with that? And to earn that, you wake up at 5 a.m. and you don't go to sleep till 11 p.m.'

The boy's enthusiasm did not fade with this question. Smiling, he said, 'Madam, is five rupees not a big sum compared to nothing? *Panch rupay se bahut kuch hota hai!* We can buy salt; we can buy chillies. If we sit idle, we cannot buy even that. Nobody gives us money in hundreds and thousands. Every drop makes an ocean.'

I was amazed at Javed's answer. A poor fisherboy had reminded me of the famous saying, 'It is better to light a candle than to curse the darkness.'

Then I remembered my friend's son wasting his time as he waited for a lucrative software job.

45

Oh Teacher, I Salute Thee

Once upon a time a teacher was more powerful than a ruler. He loved his students immensely and punished them when they were wrong. They would stay with him for ten to twelve years, helping him in all his work. He treated them like his own children. When these children grew up, they would remember the teacher and his wife and respect them throughout life. There was an unwritten rule that they had to give back to their teachers a part of their earnings later in life. The teacher felt proud of his students' progress. He never amassed wealth; his wealth was his students. Every teacher used to pray to God that his own students should overtake him in acquiring knowledge. That would be the greatest joy to him. *'Shishyad ichchet parajayam'*—the student should be better than the teacher. That system was known as Gurukula.

When I was young, we used to participate in district or state-level competitions. For this purpose, we used to travel from our home town to different places. Our teacher used to accompany us. We never stayed at hotels. He would take us to his sister's house and our entire team stayed there. Our teacher never gained any profit from the whole exercise, but he thought of us as his own family.

His sister would house and feed us without expecting anything. Now, when I look back, I feel that our system was great.

There is a very nice story of how students once held their teachers in great esteem. A mighty emperor was asked, 'You are a powerful emperor with so much of wealth, a vast kingdom and a mighty army. Your teacher is poor and does not own even a piece of land. But still when you meet him, why do you bow down and touch his dusty feet? Why do you sit below him and listen so earnestly? Why don't you summon him to the court?'

The emperor smiled and said, 'What a fool you are! My teacher is one of the richest men. The land that you talk about can be gained or lost in a war. The might of an emperor lasts only as long as he is young and healthy. The money he has can be spent, looted or destroyed. In no way is an emperor a great man. Look at the teacher. He has knowledge and, every year, he gives it to his students. The more he gives, the more he prospers. Nobody can loot his wisdom or his knowledge. No one can take it away by force or violence. He flourishes every year with more and more knowledge. Is he not a great man? All his students are like his own children and when children prosper, is not the father a wealthy man?'

This story shows the respect for the teacher and the teacher's great attachment both to knowledge and to his students. That is the reason we Indians place the teacher in the third-highest position in the social hierarchy, after the mother and the father.

Today, the Gurukula system neither exists nor is it

practical. Our government has taken enough pains and invested considerable resources to establish modern education in villages and cities. It has appointed several thousand teachers who have been trained to teach different subjects and the values of life. Their main objective is to produce better citizens for tomorrow.

Recently, I was in Orissa on work. In October 1999, there had been a great cyclone in Orissa, which nobody expected. The cyclone uprooted trees, took away roofs and destroyed buildings. The state also suffers from chronic floods. Every year, many people lose their mud houses, their cattle and other property. Statistics show that there is a rise in the number of orphans, the physically handicapped and the mentally retarded after every disaster. Orphanages thus become overcrowded. Many a time, parents simply abandon their physically handicapped and mentally retarded children. They consider them an additional burden in their poverty. Due to waterborne diseases in the aftermath of natural disasters, government hospital wards fill up with three times more patients than they can handle. Doctors, NGOs and government officials work hard, but the disasters are often too much to handle.

No government can repair schools every year. It is a Herculean task. So our Foundation decided that some of the schools we planned to build near a river should be built at an elevation, so that they could also act as a shelter during floods. We involved schoolteachers in this work and they were very proud to help us because, after all, it was their school. The system worked well with us because of the teachers' participation.

I went to inaugurate one of the shelter-cum-school complexes in an interior part of Orissa. It was early in the morning. The whole atmosphere was quite festive. The teacher who had helped us to build the school had been transferred to a neighbouring village, but he still came for the occasion.

Before the inauguration, I felt like talking to the students. When I went to one of the classes I was surprised to see that the classroom was very crowded with students. Most of the children were sitting on the floor. Only a few benches were available. I looked in the next room. It was the same. Outside, a class was being taught in the shade of a neem tree. Clearly, there was a dearth of classrooms.

I was there a little earlier than scheduled. The new principal of the school came and met me with apologies. She was a middle-aged woman, but looked quite fit. She appeared very strict, but looks are often deceptive. She said that she was very busy with the day's function. While talking to her, I saw another structure in one corner of the compound. In front of that building, a sari and a few other wet clothes had been hung out to dry.

Having been a teacher, I know that we tend to talk a lot, so I cut her short. Pointing to the sari, I asked who was staying in that building.

She was taken aback and fumbled, 'Oh, that building is a relief shelter.'

'Why is there a relief shelter in the school premises?'

'Just like yours. When there is a natural calamity, it serves as a shelter. Otherwise it is a school.'

'What is the natural calamity now?'

'There was a cyclone.'

'But that was two years back. Are people still staying here?'

She changed her tone and said, 'No, but people affected by the floods are staying there.'

That was also not true, because the floods had receded by that time. The headmistress insisted that we should not waste any more time on this matter because it was getting late for the inauguration. But I was adamant to know who was staying there. She was helpless and accompanied me.

It was a good building with several benches inside that had been arranged as a cot. There were utensils and trunks. Firewood was piled in a corner, indicating that someone was cooking here.

'Who lives here?' I asked again.

She was a little irritated but tried not to show it. 'Some adivasi students. This is used as their hostel.'

Again, this was a blatant lie because this was a boys' school while the clothes were all women's clothes. Besides, it didn't look like a dorm. When I expressed my opinion, the headmistress said nothing. She then told me, 'This building is not very good. Many of our teachers are very poor and they have to come from a great distance. So I have given them a place to stay temporarily.'

I didn't believe her.

'The teachers are paid well and also get a house rent allowance. Why would they stay in the school premises?'

I could hear a murmur behind me. Young children with

eyes wide open were looking at me. Children are the best spokespersons. They tell the truth and won't lie to please anybody. So I called a young boy and asked, '*Beta,* who is staying there?'

The boy pointed his finger at the headmistress. She bowed her head in shame.

I went to her and said, 'Why did you lie to me, that too four times, giving four different reasons? If you lie, the children learn from you and do the same. You should be a model to them. You should lead by example. You are a woman and the essential quality of a woman is compassion. When your students are crowded like animals in the classroom, how can you convert their classroom into your house? It is their building. Can't you just think like a mother? If your child had been in the same class, would you not feel bad? You are also a teacher. Is it not true that the essential quality of a teacher is to care and love the students? I am also a teacher. We should worry about our students' benefit, not ours. This is not a business house. This is a training house for the future generation. How could you use their place to save your house rent, just because these children cannot speak out against this injustice? How can you tolerate their suffering? No government official comes to this godforsaken place and checks. When these children grow up, how will they remember you? Is this not the land of great teachers?'

There was no reply.

Recently, I had to attend the birthday party of a one-year-old baby. It was arranged lavishly at a five-star hotel. I went with my friend. I didn't know what gift to give such a young child. Nowadays, giving and accepting gifts has become big business. A new equation seems to have arisen: your present should be proportional to your prosperity. The very meaning of a gift symbolizing love and affection has been lost.

There is a very beautiful saying in Gujarati: '*hishob kavadi ma, bakshees laakhma*'. It means, 'Whenever you are settling the account, you should settle up to the last paisa. But when you are giving a gift to somebody, think not of the price of the gift, but the affection behind it.' One may give a very expensive gift, but there may not be any affection behind it. On the other hand, a small gift may carry a tremendous amount of love with it.

For a one-year-old child, the only gift I could think of was a food bowl and a spoon with which he could eat. When I picked it up from the store, my friend laughed and said, 'You'll get into trouble. People will expect a bigger gift from you. Think about it before you buy.'

I repeated the Gujarati proverb and went ahead with my purchase.

We went to the hotel. Everybody who was somebody in the city had been invited. There were children, adults and old people. There were society ladies and businessmen. Kanchipurams, patolas, chiffons and matching diamonds could be seen everywhere. The total amount of gold worn at the party must have exceeded what is stocked in Tribhuvandas Bhimji Javeri, the most famous jewellery shop in Mumbai!

The usual rituals were performed—parents cutting the cake, father blowing out the first candle, mother feeding the cake to the baby, video recording of the event, bursting of balloons and singing 'Happy Birthday'. Then people started giving the gifts. This was followed by dinner.

Suited and booted men were thinking of new contacts and women were exchanging news of the latest fashions. Young teenage girls and boys were busy listening to Metallica and heading for the dance floor. Old people were complaining and talking nostalgically about the past days, or exchanging news about their illnesses and treatments. Young mothers were busy feeding their kids. The birthday boy was crying. His uncomfortable clothes were hurting him; so were the gold ornaments he had been made to wear. The bright, unfamiliar lights were scaring him. I saw the gifts given to the baby. Expensive silverware, gold chains, cash, even a laptop computer!

Many people whom I did not know came to me and started narrating the difficulties in their organizations. Everybody had the same question: 'When you are free, shall I come and meet you? We don't want money, but we want your guidance.' Experience has taught me that nobody asks for money at the first meeting; most people ask for guidance in various matters that are totally unrelated to me, like finding a suitable match for their daughter or a job for their son. They ask for various types of assistance, in cash or kind, for their social organizations. If nothing else, they want me to address some gathering. At such times, I often feel like shouting, 'Don't treat me as a machine that can be used for your benefit, treat me as human!'

Some time later I was in Ahmedabad for some work. The Law Garden Road there is popularly known as the Love Garden area. There are small shops that open only in the evenings and remain open till 11 p.m. There are open-air restaurants with chairs and tables placed on the road. It reminds me of Paris, a tourist paradise. Normally young tourists visit this place late in the evenings.

The shops are small but extremely colourful. They sell handicrafts of Gujarat. Gujarat is famous for its embroidery, such as kutch work, *chaniya cholis,* bed sheets and pillow covers. There are shops selling inexpensive silver pendants and other silver ornaments of rural design. These are enchantingly beautiful. When one sees such attractive wares, one feels tempted to buy something, unmindful of whether the items purchased will ever be worn or used.

One evening I had gone to this area to window-shop with my friends. While I was walking on the streets aimlessly, a beautiful purse embroidered in mirror work caught my eye. I liked it and asked the shopkeeper its price. The owners were a young couple probably married only two or three years earlier. The girl was charming and healthy and had a beautiful smile. She was wearing a simple cotton sari; other than a black bead chain and glass bangles, she wore no other ornaments. If a woman is healthy and smiling, she appears beautiful even without ornaments. Her husband was a little older, maybe around twenty-five, lean and tall. He said that the price of the purse was Rs 100.

My friend from Ahmedabad felt that it was too costly. She wanted to bargain. Just then, I noticed a baby, probably a year old, lying in a cradle, close to the footpath near the shop. He was dressed in a simple cotton outfit, playing with a wooden toy. The baby was healthy and cheerful. I did not see his parents around, so I asked the girl about it.

She said proudly, 'He's our baby.' Her warm smile made me want to converse with her.

'Why do you bring the baby to the market? Can't you leave him with someone at home, or with a neighbour?'

She replied hesitantly, 'I don't have anyone at home and all my neighbours are in different shops here, doing the same business.'

I always like to converse with these women and try to understand their way of living. The beautiful kutchi purse disappeared from my mind and thoughts about this baby crept in.

'How do you manage with your baby and work?'

'I wake up early in the morning and do all the embroidery work and household chores. My husband looks after the baby. In the afternoon he does the embroidery and I look after the baby. In the evening both of us look after the shop and the baby together.'

'Do you read the newspaper? Or watch TV?' These questions were quite irrelevant, but I wanted to know.

'We don't have a TV. Once in a while, we go to our neighbour's house to see it. In our *basti*, we get only one Gujarati paper, which my husband reads and tells me the news. Anyway, there is no great news every day. Some political party rules the country, somebody is murdered or there is some natural calamity. Our life will not be affected by any of these. It is the same, ever since I was a small girl. My father in Kutch used to do the same thing that my husband does now.'

'Can you read? Have you gone to a school?'

'No, I never went to school. I had a stepmother who never sent us to school. We're from Kutch. When we were children, from the very beginning, we had to learn embroidery rather than attend school. My husband has studied up to the fourth class, enough to read a Gujarati newspaper.'

'How old is your child?'

'One year. Today is his birthday. We've decided not to have any more children. Though we may not be educated, let him study and we shall work hard for him.'

By this time, the bargaining was over. The shopkeeper would not reduce the price, so my friend didn't buy the purse and we were about to move. I looked at the child again—a happy, healthy child. It was his birthday, so I suddenly remembered the birthday party at the five-star hotel. Being born in a wealthy family is merely a matter of chance. This child had been born here. I felt like giving him a gift. I opened my purse and placed a hundred rupee note in his plump hands and started walking away.

Immediately, his mother came running after me. 'Please take your money back. We're not beggars. We don't know you. Why should you give us money?'

I could see the anger on her face. I said, 'It's not for you. Today is his birthday and we have a custom: whenever a child completes a year, we give him a small gift. I talked to you for the past five minutes, so I do know you a little. I'm giving this money to the child as a blessing. Don't refuse.'

By this time, her anger had cooled. Her eyes brightened and her smile came back. I turned and was about to walk on. She caught my right hand and gave me the purse. I was shocked. I resisted accepting it.

'Are you returning what I've given the baby as a gift?'

'No *ben*, I am really amazed about the whole thing. Many customers come to our shop, but it is always about business. They ask the price and then they bargain. After they give the money, they take the packet, don't even turn back and go away. Not even once has anybody talked to us like a human being. They always treat us like business people. Nobody asks how we live, what we do. They see exactly what you saw today. You are the first person who has treated us like any other human being. That's a nice feeling. Do not get upset that I am giving you this. My child is giving you this. It felt so nice that someone who is not from my place, who does not know our language, who is unknown to us, is blessing my baby on his first birthday. Is it not our duty to respect such a lady within our capacity? God has not given me enough money to fill this empty purse, but I pray that God will shower enough fortune on you to fill up many purses.'

I could identify totally with her desire to be treated as a human being and not as some faceless machine. I accepted the gift happily. The child was still smiling and playing with his toy, oblivious to us.

47

An Unknown Benefactor from Chennai

The concept of fund-raising is extremely popular in the USA. There are separate departments in universities and charitable organizations for this activity. They catch the right fish by different methods so that donors give money to the organization or university concerned. This notion is now catching on in India too.

My friend Mythili works for an NGO. She is a fund-raiser, smart and talkative, hailing from a middle-class family. One morning, she called up asking me to accompany her to the house of a very affluent person, a lady who was well known in the city. Mythili had been approaching this woman for a donation. At last, the lady had agreed to meet Mythili in her farmhouse forty kilometres away from the city. Mythili was a little hesitant to go alone and so she asked me to accompany her.

We reached the palatial house. It was built on a huge twenty-five acre plot and was surrounded by a beautiful garden. The house was built in the traditional cottage model. There was strict security and we were asked a number of questions. Only after confirming our appointment over the intercom did the guard let us in.

Though it had a rustic look from the outside, the house was gorgeous and modern inside. All the walls were painted in pastel shades. There was a pond with a fountain sprinkling scented water. It seemed to bring nature into that big hall. The wooden floor and antique objects added to the charm. There was also a terrace garden.

The lady of the house was sitting on a swing hung by shining chains. She looked gorgeous in a chiffon sari and platinum ornaments. From a distance, she made a gesture telling us to sit down. Though in her mid-fifties, she looked much younger. There was the aroma of sandalwood all around. Fresh flowers were kept in vases. Two smart-looking secretaries were next to her. Both Mythili and I felt very uncomfortable because the most important things in life—the smile and warmth—were missing here. I have always observed that it is not the food, nor the ornaments, nor the house, but a host's genuine warmth that puts guests at ease and opens the gateway to friendship, irrespective of status, age, gender and language.

Mythili talked about her NGO, of course everything in superlative terms as befitted her mission. Ultimately, she has to sell her ideas. The lady listened patiently, not showing any reaction. When people don't show any reaction, the person on the other side of the table often becomes tongue-tied. Shrewd people never allow anyone to read their mind. Simple-minded people talk a lot, open their heart and reveal what they are, which is exactly what Mythili did. The other lady revealed nothing at all.

After an unbearable silence, she said, 'Give your papers to my secretary. I will go through them and get back to you.'

Our balloon of enthusiasm was pricked by that answer. After all, she could have said this over the phone. We drove back all the way, having wasted half a day's work.

I met Mythili a month later at a school opening ceremony where the same would-be donor was the chief guest. I asked Mythili about the donation.

Mythili took me aside and told me in hushed tones, 'It's very difficult to get money out of her. She is ready to spend any amount of money on herself, but she thinks ten thousand times before giving to a charity. You know, after I wooed her for a month she finally agreed to give Rs 10,000 on the condition that we invite her for this function as the chief guest, put her photo in the paper and give a press release about her.'

'You shouldn't have asked her for such a small amount.'

'Please remember that raising funds for an NGO is very difficult. You don't have the same experience. Every rupee counts. Is it not true that every drop of water makes an ocean? Nobody donates money without expecting something in return. This is the lesson I've learnt in fund-raising.'

Since I had no experience in fund-raising, I had to accept what Mythili said.

Some time later I returned to work after having been on leave for a week. I dreaded coming back to my office because of the number of letters and emails that would have piled up while I was away. I was busy sorting out letters when my secretary took out a small envelope. There was an expression of surprise on her face.

'What is so surprising in that envelope?'

She showed me a small handwritten note. It said, 'I know that you do not know me. I read about your work in the newspapers. I read your articles as well. When a writer really experiences life, only then can he or she write about it. Language is just a tool but in no way can good language alone make a readable article. It is the personal experience along with suitable language that makes an article interesting to read. By reading your experiences, I have realized what kind of work you do and how passionately you do it . . .'

I was busy so I handed the note back to my secretary and said impatiently, 'This is just one of those exaggerated letters of appreciation. Just file it. You don't need to show me such things. Morning time is very precious in the office.'

'Ma'am, did you read it completely? This is something different.'

I took the note back and continued reading. 'I am old and cannot travel like you. I have saved some money. I would like to give it to you so that you can use it in your work. You may have much more, but this is my contribution to your work. I will not ask to whom you give it or how you use it. I have confidence in you.'

A draft for Rs 4,00,000 was attached to the note.

Now I was even more surprised than my secretary. In my public life, I have received hundreds of applications asking for money and many letters telling me that the money I have donated is insufficient. But here was a person spontaneously giving me money for my work. There was not a single demand. I held up the draft. It was like a star shining in the dark blue sky.

I asked my secretary whether she knew the person who had written the note and donated such a large sum, but she did not. The donor had neither written anything about himself nor given any contact details. From the postmark we knew that the letter was from Chennai.

I bow to this unknown donor from Chennai with great respect. I remembered the poem about Abu Ben Adam and prayed, 'May his tribe increase.'

My mind went back to the rich lady whom Mythili had approached. How different the two donors were!

48

Life is an Examination

Sumitra and Suresh were my classmates. Sumitra was bright and sharp in her youth. She was dynamic and pushy. She used to top the class in her studies. Suresh was not as bright as Sumitra, but he was a very nice person. They fell in love and got married. Suresh earned lots of money through business. Sumitra lent a helping hand in managing the business. Even though they were well off, Sumitra would never spend money unnecessarily. She knew the value of money and hard work.

I used to meet them once in a while, maybe at a get-together at their place. They were perfect hosts. We would all sit on their lawn remembering our golden days. Outwardly, they looked happy, the perfect couple, made for each other. But there was always a trace of sadness. They had no children, and they had decided not to adopt a child for reasons of their own.

One day Sumitra called me with an invitation. 'Can you come over for dinner in the evening?'

I thought that it was one of their usual parties, but when I entered their house I felt tension. They were both looking tired and worried and not at all themselves.

As soon as Sumitra saw me she broke down. 'Today I went for a medical check-up. It was a routine check-up, that's what I thought. But my doctor says there is a problem with my kidney. I'm really worried.'

Death, a five-letter word, scares everyone. The person may be a king, a billionaire, a pauper or a beggar. But there is nobody who can escape death. I could easily understand Sumitra's and Suresh's worries. The previous year Suresh had had a heart attack. They were entirely dependent on each other. Now the time had come when they did not know how long they would survive. In life, nothing can be equated with health. Good health is the greatest asset. Money can buy medicine and comfort, but not happiness. They wanted me to listen to their worries and I did so wholeheartedly.

Suresh was very practical. 'Look, now we must think of how we should spend money in the remaining years. We should write our will so that later on there won't be any problem among the relatives. No relative helped us in our difficult period, so I don't want to give anything to any of them.'

Suresh was right. When a person earns money through hard work, his personality is different, whereas if he inherits money without hard work, he will not be strong. But Sumitra had a different opinion. It was the first time that I saw Sumitra opposing her husband. Though it was a cool night, their heated arguments raised the temperature in the room. I did not interfere in their discussion. It was their personal matter and their money. How could an outsider like me get involved? I thought it better not even to witness such things, so I decided to leave.

Sumitra stopped me and said, 'We called you for

suggestions. You've been dear and impartial to us. Don't consider yourself an outsider.'

So I had to stay and listen to both their arguments.

'I have never spent money on myself. I don't know how long I will live. Let me enjoy life the way I want.' This was Sumitra's argument.

No conclusion was drawn on that day.

Days passed. I could see a rift between the couple. I used to see and hear about Sumitra more than I did of Suresh. She started buying very fashionable clothes regardless of whether they suited her or not. I saw her photos in the society pages.

Once, when I was returning from a trip, I ran into her at the Mumbai airport. I could not believe my eyes. Was she the same Sumitra, the Sumitra of long hair and cotton saris? Now she was dressed in transparent Western clothes, dripping diamonds all over—bracelets, earrings, rings and chains. Her face had half an inch of make-up and she was drenched in perfume.

She explained why she was in Mumbai. 'I was here for a horse race. I had never seen a horse race before, so I thought, let me have that experience. From here I'm flying to Chennai to attend the wedding of a film producer's daughter.'

'Since when have you started moving in the same circles as film producers?'

'Of late, I've started financing movies. It's a great field. I was not even aware of it. I spent all my life without enjoying so many things. Now I'm busier than before.'

'How is Suresh?'

She was unhappy with my question. 'He is, as usual, immersed in his business.'

Now I realized that both of them were leading their lives independently. Suresh called me a few times to ask about certain educational institutions. Because of my experience, I gave him my sincere opinion.

After a few days, Suresh's lawyer called me up. 'Suresh has made his final will and he wants you to be the executor. Is this acceptable to you?'

I was surprised about Suresh's decision. Neither was I his relative nor did I have any business association with him. I thought that I should go and meet him. One of the most important responsibilities in life is to handle somebody else's money. You can afford to lose your own money, but if you are a trustee of any organization then your responsibilities are a thousand times greater. Trust is one of the most precious qualities you can find in this world.

I met Suresh at his home. Sumitra was away in Delhi. He was alone and cheerful, talking to his lawyer. When I read the will, I was surprised. He wanted to fund scholarships and make donations to educational institutes, libraries and computer centres. But nowhere did he want his name to be mentioned. All donations were in Sumitra's name.

I raised my eyebrows.

'Yes,' he explained. 'We may differ in our ideas. But without her help, I would not have built my business. She has her own opinions, but this is the way I look at it.'

'Is Sumitra aware of this will?'

'No. Please don't tell her about this.'

After a week's time, I came to know that Sumitra's condition was very serious. She was dead before I could reach the hospital. I also came to know that her bank balance was nil. Suresh seemed to take his dear wife's death very well. They had been married for a very long time, so I imagined how hard it must be for him to live without her. After a year, Suresh's lawyer called me and informed me that he had passed away in his sleep.

Thus the lives of two of my great friends, two individuals, ended within the span of one year. Whenever I look at the Sumitra Memorial Prize, I am faced with a question: is life not strange? Both of them knew that they would die, but chose two different paths. Sumitra was brighter than Suresh, but did not understand life the way Suresh understood it. She opted to enjoy life, whereas Suresh opted for philanthropic deeds. The same set of circumstances brought two different results from two different individuals.

49

MY MONEY, YOUR MONEY

I always feel that I am young at heart, irrespective of my age. The reason is that I am a teacher, so I mix with the younger generation. Their energy is contagious. They share their secrets with me. They are my inspiration. I teach in a college and I meet many students in each batch. Over a period of time I might not remember their names, but they remember me. Many a time they have helped me in critical situations, such as in an airport or in a hotel when I don't have reservations. They remember that I was their teacher and do their best to help me. It gives me enormous happiness to meet and talk to my old students. No wonder old wine, old memories and old students are so precious and rare.

About a decade ago, I was teaching computer science to postgraduate students. In that batch there were many bright students and among them were Ashok and Anitha. I liked them a lot. They were very sincere and hard-working. One day, after their graduation, both of them came and met me. They wanted to take up teaching as a career. They asked my opinion.

'If you love teaching and have a passion for it, only then take it up. Today, in the software industry, both of you can earn high salaries, which no college can match.

However, money won't give you the same satisfaction you get in teaching. If you don't like teaching and take it up, it will be an unwise move. If a teacher makes a mistake, an entire class is affected and so is the future of all those students.'

Anitha and Ashok still opted for teaching. When they were married, I went to their wedding and blessed them wholeheartedly. Now they were teachers like me.

Time passed and they had a baby girl. Ashok bought a scooter. They were a small, happy family settled in a rented two-bedroom house, like any educated middle-class family. Ashok's widowed mother stayed with them. Overall, their life looked serene, filled with happiness and laughter.

Though Anitha and I were colleagues now, we met rarely since our timings were different. One day, I met her in the computer lab. She looked worried and unhappy. 'Ma'am, our owner wants the house back. I feel the story may repeat itself in any rented house. It's better if we have our own house. My daughter has grown up now. I have to register her at the toddler's play school. I cannot drop her by scooter because of the clash of timings. My mother-in-law is old and has arthritis. We require a maid to help her. There are so many financial demands.'

I understood her problem and nodded. After all, I too had undergone the whole cycle and much more in my younger days.

She continued, 'I have decided to take up a job in a software company that will pay more. Ashok says he's very happy teaching and doesn't want to shift, but I feel that one of us has to take a better-paying job. What does it matter who takes up the job? There is no difference between Ashok and me. Together we make a unit. It doesn't matter who earns what. Ashok is a very supportive and understanding husband, and my mother-in-law is a great lady. I have started applying for jobs in software companies. Can I give your name as a reference?'

She was logical and practical. I agreed that she could give my name as a reference. As soon as she got a job, she called up and thanked me.

After three years, I received an email from her inviting me to her house-warming ceremony. I was happy for her and went to the function. It was a compact three-bedroom house with all the modern amenities. She was looking very confident and happy. I was the last guest to leave, so she had some time to talk to me.

'Ma'am, this is the result of my hard work. I saved every single rupee for this house. Today, I have built the house and I feel nobody can remove us from here.'

'How is your job?'

'It's great. Very demanding, but I enjoy it. In three years, I have been made the group leader and five people report to me. I work long hours. The company has sent me to the USA twice, each time for a period of three months.'

'How do you manage all these things, with your child?'

'My mother-in-law and the maid manage my daughter. My maid is extremely efficient. Of course, Ashok is also there to supervise.'

Some time later, I saw her in a new Opel Astra car in

Jayanagar with her 'extremely efficient' maid. The maid was well dressed and was holding the hand of Anitha's five-year-old child. Anitha was happy to meet me, but I was surprised by her appearance. She looked different. She wore an expensive sari, shining diamond droplets and nearly a dozen gold bangles. And, beneath her make-up, her face showed some arrogance. Was it over-confidence or a shade of rudeness? I couldn't tell.

Anitha was excited. 'Ma'am, I got employee stock option shares from my company. I cashed part of it and bought a car. I took my family, along with the maid, to Singapore for a holiday. I've told Ashok to come with me, along with the child, when I next visit the USA. Anyway the company pays for the dependents. Isn't it great?'

Yes. It was great. But something was missing.

'How's Ashok?'

In a tone tinged with a little unhappiness she replied, 'He's still in college, teaching the same old stuff. He got a promotion recently, a small hike of just five hundred rupees. Ma'am, you should tell Ashok that he's wasting his time in a college. He can get a better job than mine. He's brighter than I am. But he won't listen to me. Maybe the academic field has made him too soft.'

'Anitha, everyone is grown up and they know what they want.'

She didn't like my answer.

Later, I happened to meet Ashok at a teachers' workshop. It was lunch break and we had some free time.

'Sorry to barge in on you with my personal problems,

but you're the only person whom Anitha and I have known fairly well for a long time. You have seen us as students and as colleagues. Your advice and your opinion matter a lot to me.'

'Did Anitha ask you to talk to me?' I inquired, remembering my earlier meeting with Anitha.

'No. I'm extremely unhappy with my marriage. Many a time, I wonder whether I should stay married or separate.'

'Ashok, don't be silly. There are always differences of opinion in a couple, particularly when they're young. Those who say there's no difference of opinion are not really husband and wife,' I joked. I wanted to release the tension and ease the problem with humour.

Ashok was not affected by my humour. 'No, ma'am. Anitha now feels her job is better and she acts superior. She looks down upon other people. Everything is just "me" for her now. Like, "I bought this house with my money," and "with my ESOP shares, I bought a car". She behaves as though she can buy everything with the money she earned by selling her shares. The share price of the IT company she works for keeps rising, so no wonder ESOP is a boon to employees. But it's bringing unhappiness in our family. She doesn't respect my old mother as she used to do before.'

'Why?' I asked foolishly.

'Because she can be replaced by an efficient maid. Anitha feels she can get what I earn for the entire year simply by selling a few of her shares. She keeps telling me all the time that she's better than I am. I cannot live with a wife who's got such an attitude.'

'But Ashok, suppose you were in her position. Wouldn't there be any problems then? Can you not accept your wife earning more than you? Maybe it's hurting your ego.'

Ashok thought for a while and replied, 'To some extent you may be right, ma'am. More than that, if the roles had been reversed and I went on harping about "my money", then definitely she would have felt bad. Between husband and wife there shouldn't be any difference. One shouldn't respect the other partner just because he or she earns more. But what hurts me is that she ignores my support. If people get a lot of money in a short time, they act the way Anitha is acting now. Money should come slowly over a period of time. Then only does one respect it. Whether it's a man or a woman, earning too much money in too short a period is as bad as excess liquor.'

I didn't have an answer. I was lost in an ocean of thoughts. Money is a double-edged knife that can be used to cut a fruit and also to kill a person. It's important to earn money, but how you handle it is much more important. If Anitha had been mature, she would have thanked the people around her who cooperated with her. She would have said 'we' instead of 'I'. She would have said, 'With my husband's support, I have built this house.'

50

IS LIFE FAIR?

When a person suffers physically, people sympathize with him or her. When someone is mentally ill, on the other hand, people in our country think differently. Mental disease is a taboo subject in our society. We never consider that mental health is as important or even more important than physical health.

I was working with a psychiatrist who specializes in treating mental diseases. I was helping her rehabilitate patients. Treatment alone is not enough; it is equally important to rehabilitate these patients. Normally people presume that a mentally ill patient will always remain mentally ill. A mentally ill patient is often considered a mad person in our society.

My doctor friend, Kusuma, tells me of many such instances. These true stories are heart-rending and, at times, also amusing. It seems that once at a party, Kusuma met a woman who was well known in society. A few years earlier, Kusuma had treated this lady for depression and cured her completely. Kusuma was happy to see her and went to greet her. But as soon as this woman saw Kusuma, she walked away. Kusuma was taken aback, having expected a warm welcome. After some time, the host introduced Kusuma to all the guests. This lady behaved as if she didn't know Kusuma at all.

After the party was over, she came and apologized. 'Doctor, you should excuse me for seeming indifferent towards you. You have given me a new life, but I didn't want to recognize you in the presence of so many people. Everybody knows you are a psychiatrist. They will guess that I was once your patient and may think I am still mad.'

She left in tears as Kusuma looked on helplessly.

Once, I wanted to discuss some low-technology projects that could employ patients and give them a source of income, so I went to Kusuma's clinic. The receptionist asked me to wait as there was a patient inside. In the waiting room, I saw an old couple sitting next to me. There were no smiles on their faces. They looked very worried. Their clothes showed that they were affluent. The patient was probably their daughter. I then thought that children's mental health brings much more happiness to parents than money.

After some time, the patient came out and I entered Kusuma's chamber. I forgot my ideas of rehabilitation as thoughts about this couple troubled me. I wondered what their problem was and asked Kusuma, but she wouldn't tell me as it would have been a breach of trust. However, she did narrate a few incidents about patients whose identity she did not disclose.

'One of my patients, Maya, came from a cultured background. She was married into a highly educated but less cultured family. It was an arranged marriage where the groom's job was more important than cultural compatibility. She was married to Jagadish, and his sisters and mother were always cruel to her. It was surprising that Jagadish, who was in a good position, was scared of his mother and extremely obedient. The mother took advantage of the situation and would always trouble the innocent daughter-in-law. Jagadish was more his mother's boy than Maya's husband.'

'Kusuma, this is the story in most homes. How many women have suffered in the same way!'

'That's true. Social pressures are high. Many a time, films and TV serials give too much importance to marriage and finding a husband.'

'How did Maya react?'

'Maya tried her level best, like any other Indian woman, to adjust to her in-laws. She worked hard to establish a good relationship. She always felt that one day or the other, her in-laws would change. But when she became convinced that her husband would never take her side, she went into depression. A woman wants her husband to love her. For that, she will be ready to face anything. But once she knows that she will not get this love, she feels utterly disappointed.'

I imagined the young and sensitive Maya going through all these trials. It takes time to recover from mental agony. She might have come and cried many times to Kusuma.

'What treatment did you give Maya?'

'I called Jagadish and his mother, explained to them that what Maya needed was tender love and care, not money. They never understood. He is the principal of a college, but does not understand the simple philosophy of love. He is acclaimed as a great teacher on paper, but his wife is a mental patient. I called Maya's parents and told them there seemed to be no hope that Jagadish would care for their daughter. Maya should realize that and start to live her own life without depending on her husband's love. It was very hard for them to accept this, but as a doctor it was my duty to tell the truth.'

'What happened to Maya?'

'I treated Maya for a long time, over several counselling sessions, many anti-depression tablets, and now she's all right. She is back with her parents.'

'Kusuma, isn't it unfair? Jagadish is the bad person but poor Maya had to undergo the treatment? The person causing the problem is happy and through no fault of hers, Maya suffers. What is worse is that society will blame Maya for leaving her husband.'

'Yes, who says life is fair? Life is always unfair. If you want, you can make it fair.'

51

THREE BRIGHT YOUNG MEN

M any years ago, I was the chief guest at a function. This was held in a hostel for poor students that had been built by a philanthropist. Food and shelter were free, but students had to bear other expenses like tuition and clothing.

In my younger days, I have come across many families who would look after students who were economically backward but otherwise bright. They used to help them with their fees or clothing and often with their food as well. In those days, most colleges were located in larger towns. Many poor students who came to study in these towns used to stay with these families and would be treated as part of the family. The woman of the house considered this a good deed and helped the poor students wholeheartedly. Today, the situation is different. Even smaller towns have schools and colleges, so this custom has disappeared.

While I was sitting on the dais, I remembered the past and congratulated the person who had built the hostel. It was a good deed and of great help to many students. The hostel secretary told me about some of the students in the hostel who had secured ranks but had a problem paying their tuition fees.

He said, 'Madam, this year we have three students from different disciplines who have secured ranks. All of them are from extremely poor families. They have one more year to complete their degrees.'

'What are they studying?'

'One is in medicine, the second in engineering and the third in commerce.'

'Can I meet them after the function?'

The function went on as usual. Often, at such functions, too much praise is lavished on the chief guest. Sometimes, they even make exaggerated and false claims about the chief guest. I feel this unnecessary praising is the highest form of corruption where people are easily fooled, and it encourages those who are praised to develop an inflated opinion of themselves. That's why in the twelfth century, in Karnataka, the great revolutionary leader Basaveshwara warned in his teaching that praise is like golden gallows.

After the function, I met the three poor bright boys whom the secretary had told me about. They were a little puzzled, shy and nervous. All of them had the same story: father in a small job unable to make ends meet, a large family back in the village, no land or any other asset. Only sheer determination to excel in studies had brought them here against all odds.

I felt sorry for them. There are many parents who struggle to give their children the best of education with tuitions, coaching and plenty of books. But here were these eager, hard-working students who were struggling to pay their fees. Perhaps Saraswati, the goddess of learning, liked them.

'Please call on me in June. I will help you with your fees,' I promised.

They did not expect this and I could see the happiness on their faces.

As promised, I paid their fees and forgot about the whole incident. Some years later I was going abroad and wanted to buy a sari for a friend who lived there. I remembered it on the way to the airport and stopped at a sari shop on the way. It was lunchtime, so hardly anybody was in the shop. It was very quiet. I was in a hurry, so I quickly selected a sari that was on display and asked one of the salesmen to pack a similar one and get me the bill.

Suddenly, a young gentleman appeared from the back of the shop. He was well dressed, charming and sophisticated. He smiled at me and invited me to sit in his office. I didn't know who he was. I thought he might be one of my ex-students. Many a time I cannot remember their names, particularly if they were in undergraduate classes.

I stepped into his office. It was well furnished—fresh-cut flowers, marble flooring, latest modern artwork on the walls, electronic gadgets and the whole works. In a nutshell, it was an affluent office.

'I'm in a hurry to go to the airport. I want the packet immediately,' I told him. I opened my purse and gave the money for the sari. I didn't sit down and insisted that I must leave immediately.

The young man smiled and said, 'Please sit down, ma'am. Your packet will be ready any moment.'

I wondered when this young man had passed out of

our college. 'Which year did I teach you?' I asked, trying to place him in a batch I had taught.

'No, ma'am, I was not your student.'

'But you know me?'

'Yes, I met you a few years ago in the student hostel.'

I was unable to remember him.

'You had come there as a chief guest,' he reminded me. 'I met you with two of my friends. You paid my final year B.Com fees.'

Now I did remember him. He had been one of those bright-eyed and nervous young boys, so different from what I saw today.

I felt happy. 'What are you doing now?'

'Ma'am, I am manager and partner in this sari shop. God is very kind. We are doing good business.'

'Where is your family?'

'I am married and settled here. My two brothers are students and live with me. My two sisters are married. My parents are very happy.'

By then my packet had been delivered to me and I got up to leave. He came right up to the car to say goodbye. It was getting late so I rushed and just made it to the aircraft. As the flight took off, I wanted to ensure the sari was good and opened the bag. I was surprised. There were two saris. I had wanted to buy only one and had paid for only one. And the packet contained not only two saris, but also the money that I had paid, along with a small note.

'Ma'am,' the note read, 'it was very kind that you paid for my fees without knowing me. Many times, I have wondered why you did that. I was a total stranger and not related to you at all. You never expected anything from me. Now, I have made it a point to help people who are not related to me, without any expectation. This is my small gift to you. It may not be a big thing, but I would like to give it with affection and gratitude. You have changed my life.'

I was touched by his words and tears filled my eyes.

I reached Mumbai. My international flight was delayed due to a technical problem, so I thought I would go and buy some snacks at the Santa Cruz market. While walking on the footpath with a friend, I stumbled and fell down. My foot swelled up. I was worried that it might be fractured. My friend lived in Mumbai, so she took me to a doctor close by. She assured me that though he was a little expensive, he was very good.

We went to this doctor in Khar. The clinic was modern, the receptionist was smart and professional. She asked whether I had an appointment and when I said no, she asked me to wait. She talked to the doctor and then sent us in. The doctor was young and very confident. I felt at ease. He made me comfortable with his smile. While he was examining my leg, he started a conversation.

'Ma'am, I have met you before. You look older now.'

'Where have you met me before?'

'I was in a student hostel. You had come there as a chief guest. After the function, I met you with my two other friends.'

I guessed who he was but wanted to reconfirm. 'Where are your friends now?'

'One is in Bangalore, a partner in a sari shop, and the other is in the US. How come you are here?'

I explained the reason. By that time, he knew what was wrong with my leg.

'Don't worry. It's not a fracture, just a torn ligament. You'll be all right with medicine.'

I was happy that this boy was doing well and was also relieved that there was no fracture.

While I was about to leave, I asked him, 'Are you married?'

With the same confident smile he replied, 'Yes. My wife is also a doctor and we have settled here.' Then he called the next patient in.

When I came out, the telephone on the receptionist's desk buzzed. Probably the doctor was talking to the receptionist. Maybe he was telling her not to collect any fees, but I wanted to pay. He had just started a clinic in such a posh area and was also married. I wanted to encourage him.

I opened my purse. The receptionist said, 'It's Rs 300.'

'Isn't that a bit too much?' I was surprised and my hand was still inside the purse.

'No. The doctor himself told me the amount. Yours was not a confirmed appointment.'

I paid the bill and left.

I had helped three people at the same time without expecting anything in return, but their attitudes were so different. One person felt grateful for my help and wanted to help others in a similar manner. The other didn't even mention the help he had received from me and felt neither grateful for it nor obliged to me. He treated me exactly as he would have treated a perfect stranger. When people with different ideas face the same situation, they act differently.

I have yet to meet the third one who is in the USA.